THE
ILLUSTRATED ENCYCLOPAEDIA
OF ANIMAL LIFE

THE ANIMAL KINGDOM

The strange and wonderful ways of mammals, birds, reptiles, fishes and insects. A new and authentic natural history of the wild life of the world

VOLUME 3

FREDERICK DRIMMER, M.A.
EDITOR-IN-CHIEF

GEORGE G. GOODWIN
*Associate Curator of Mammals,
The American Museum of Natural
History*

CHARLES M. BOGERT
*Curator of Amphibians and Reptiles,
The American Museum of Natural
History*

DEAN AMADON
E. THOMAS GILLIARD
*Associate Curators of Birds,
The American Museum of Natural History*

CHRISTOPHER W. COATES *Curator*
JAMES W. ATZ *Assistant Curator*
*Aquarium of the New York Zoological
Society*

JOHN C. PALLISTER
Research Associate, Insects, The American Museum of Natural History

ODHAMS BOOKS LIMITED, LONG ACRE, LONDON

THE PIKA—A BUSY WORKER

The pika is an eater of green vegetables. Since it does not sleep through the long, cold winter that visits its mountain home, it must make provision for the lean days of famine. Even the bitter icy winds and severe frosts that split the rocks about its den cannot drive the pika from its lofty realm to the sheltered valleys below.

When the days begin to grow short in the autumn, the little harvester gathers its crop of green vegetation and grass and spreads it out on the rocks to dry and cure in the sun. Should an unpredictable storm threaten to wet the drying harvest, the entire colony of pikas will turn out in force, gather the hay into bundles, and lug it away to the safety of their dens.

If necessary, these busy little workers will stay at work until far into the night. The harvest means life to them, and full well they know it.

Spring comes late in the land of the little pikas, and it is May or June before the first young are born. Three or four are about the average number in a litter, and litters continue to arrive until the beginning of September.

Pikas breed around the world. In North America there are three principal kinds of these little mountaineers; they are mostly greyish or buff in colour. The Rocky Mountain Pika dwells in the mountains from British Columbia to Arizona, while the Grey-headed Pika occurs at high elevations in California, Oregon, Idaho, Nevada and Utah. The Collared Pika is a greyish animal occupying the cold, bleak mountain ranges of Alaska and the Yukon.

Of the Old World species the Himalayan Pika is the largest. There are many other pikas at home in the Altai Mountains of Siberia, in China, Mongolia, and northern India.

TRUE HARES AND RABBITS

Large, long ears, a short tail, very long hind limbs and feet, thick soft fur—it is by these features that we recognize the hares and the rabbits. Yet how can we tell the two apart? Earlier, we saw there is more than a little confusion in the use of the names "rabbits" and "hares". "Rabbit" was originally applied to a European species that lives underground in communal burrows, or warrens, and brings forth its babies naked, blind, and helpless. On the other hand, in the true hares of the genus *Lepus*, the young (they are called leverets) have their eyes wide open, are fully clothed in soft, warm fur, and are active at birth. They are born (kindled) in a "form", or surface nest, and never go underground as adults, unlike the true rabbits. Hares are larger than rabbits.

Still, these distinctions are not generally known. A number of animals, such as the jack rabbit and the snowshoe rabbit, are really hares; some, such as the cottontail, are neither rabbits nor hares, strictly speaking. But once a name has grown popular with laymen, it becomes practically impossible to eliminate it from common usage.

Hares average about twenty-five inches in head-and-body length, and often have very big ears; sometimes these are seven inches in length.

The animals have a fairly long tail, which, except for the white on the underside, is more or less concealed in the fur. The exceedingly long hind limbs and feet enable the fastest of them to travel at forty-five miles per hour. The true hares make their home in Europe, Asia, Africa, and North America.

HOW TO RECOGNIZE THEIR TRACKS

Rabbit and hare tracks are distinctive and can never be confused with those of any other animal. Moving slowly or at full speed, a hare or rabbit never walks, but travels in a series of leaps. The hop may be lengthened but the pattern of the tracks is always about the same: in front are two large imprints side by side; centrally lined up at the rear are two smaller prints, one behind the other.

THE ANCIENT RABBIT

With an ancestral lineage dating back some thirty million years, wild rabbits have spread over most of the large land masses of the earth. They have not reached southern South America, which is surprising, since introduced European rabbits and hares have become well established there.

Despite their great antiquity, the rabbits conform closely to a general standard pattern throughout their wide range, though they may vary in size from the great Alaska Hare to the Pygmy Idaho Rabbit. Only the Hispid Hare, *Caprolagus*, from the Himalayan foothills, has comparatively harsh, coarse fur. They are all vegetarians and live on land, some dwelling in burrows in the ground.

The probable length of life for rabbits in general is not more than ten or twelve years with full protection. Few wild rabbits live for more than three or four years; cottontails are old at three years.

GREAT WHITE HARES

It is odd that we should find the largest of all the hares in a most forbidding climate. Weighing up to nine pounds or even more, and two feet long, the Arctic, Polar, or Snow Hare makes its home as far north as the snow-sheeted, treeless wastes that lie along the Arctic ice-cap.

In northern Europe and Siberia its range extends south into wooded regions at all seasons of the year, but in America it travels below the timber line during the winter only.

The Arctic hare is well adapted to its life in the Far North. All through the winter its fur is snow white, except for black tips on its moderately sized ears. A prowling enemy would have to be very sharp-sighted to spot it on the icy plains; even the hungry wolf and fox and the snowy owl are often deceived. The hare changes its coat with the seasons, wearing one brownish or greyish in colour during the short summer months when the snow has left the tundra. It makes this change by moulting and not by altering the pigment of the hair.

Battles at Mating Time. Springtime, bringing new energy, also brings enmity and distrust among the Arctic hares as the mating season begins. After a winter of friendly relationships, the males now snap angrily at each other; often, with their teeth and claws, they rip chunks of hair from their neighbour's throats. Standing on their hind legs, they will box furiously. When the two-weeks' mating period is over, the bands of hares break up, dispersing in ones and twos over the Arctic tundra. The doe has only one litter, with about four young on an average, and they come a month or so after mating time.

The Arctic hare does not sleep in a hole in the ground: its bed is out in the open on the wind-swept Arctic wastes. Only during a blizzard, severest of all weather, will the animal seek the friendly shelter of a willow or alder thicket.

There are three principal groups of Polar hares: the American Arctic Hare, *Lepus arcticus*, the Greenland Hare, *Lepus groenlandicus* and the Eurasian Varying Hare, *Lepus timidus*. The latter is known in Europe as the Mountain Hare or Blue Hare. In Greenland the Arctic hare joins in social gatherings of thirty to forty individuals.

AMERICAN JACK RABBITS

The White-tailed Jack Rabbit, or Prairie Hare, *Lepus townsendii*, second in size only to the Arctic hare, is a heavy-bodied hare (not a rabbit!), usually with a white tail at all seasons of the year. In the summer it wears a coat of yellowish buff; in winter it is pure white except for the black tips on the great ears. It lives in the Rocky Mountain region up to ten thousand feet in altitude and from the great plains of Saskatchewan to the border of New Mexico.

The white-tailed jack rabbit is one of the fleetest animals on the western plains; it can easily outrun a fox or coyote. Twelve feet is a single normal running hop, but if necessary the leap can be lengthened to eighteen or twenty feet. The jack rabbit lopes along at an evidently easy gait of thirty-five miles an hour; forty-five miles an hour is top speed.

Jack rabbits almost never dig shelters in the earth: normally they rest in depressions in the surface of the ground. In the north they will make a burrow in the snow to escape the winter's extreme cold. They are not particular about what they eat: anything will do, so long as it is green vegetation. They are great destroyers of alfalfa crops.

——Enemies of the Rabbit. White-tailed jacks are talented leapers. They have a high jump of at least five and one-half feet. Not all of these leaps are due to exuberance. Some are definitely observational— the creature's purpose is to get a view of the surrounding country and spot possible foes.

Many animals prey on this rabbit. The coyote used to be one of its worst enemies. However, for years now, open warfare has been waged on the coyote, and, as its numbers have dropped, those of the jack rabbit have multiplied.

When an overabundance of jacks threatens crops, every man, woman, and child of a district may be enlisted in a rabbit drive. Long lines of beaters sweep forward to herd the jack rabbits into corrals, where they are destroyed by the hundreds or even thousands. A rabbit drive in North Dakota netted 7,550 of these creatures from an area of thirty square miles.

——FIGHTING FOR A MATE. Jack rabbits are famous for the combats they engage in at breeding time. The mating season begins in early spring and lasts until midsummer in the north and from January to September in the south. There is considerable fighting between the bucks for possession of the does, and many of the males show scars and ripped ears. The young come about six weeks later. They are born in a scraped-out depression, lined with the mother's fur, under an overhanging bush or tall grass.

Newborn jack rabbits weigh from two to six ounces and broods may contain from one to eight young; four is near the average. They are clad in mottled brownish fur and have their eyes fully open. Five minutes after birth they are ready to nurse.

When the mother leaves her babies, she covers them with the grass and fur of the nest. She returns merely to nurse them, and then only under cover of darkness. When the babies are but a few days old, they begin to forage for themselves—in three or four weeks they are independent of the mother. Several litters are raised each year.

——RABBIT DANCES. The white-tailed jack rabbit likes a social gathering. On moonlit nights in mid-winter, when unseasonably warm weather has melted the snow, the author has seen ten or twelve of them together, enjoying what seemed to be some sort of ritual or social dance. Their frolicking apparently followed a regular pattern. They gathered in a great circle that gradually grew smaller as they closed in, when they would suddenly bounce high in the air and disappear in all directions. In a matter of minutes another circle would form and vanish again in similar manner.

Migrations are rare among the jack rabbits. One has been recorded where thousands were seen together moving down from high country to the lowlands into the face of a heavy snowstorm.

The White-sided Jack Rabbit, *Lepus callotis*, is perhaps the strangest hare on the North American continent. It owes this distinction to a curious trick that it can play with its coat.

This creature, otherwise brown, has ears that are totally white— there are no black tips, as in so many other jack rabbits. It also has a whitish area covering the lower sides of its body. The astounding fact is that the animal can shift the white area on the lower sides around at will by the contraction of certain skin muscles. Thus it can transfer the brown fur on the back to one side or the other and replace it by white side fur, even when the animal is travelling at a fast pace.

When an enemy approaches, the white area is always pulled on to the side that faces the intruder. As the jack rabbit zigzags on its course, the coat is correspondingly switched from side to side. In bright sunlight the white side flashes a brilliant signal that can be seen from afar, possibly a warning to other jack rabbits of approaching danger.

The territory of the white-sided jack rabbit extends from southern Arizona to Oaxaca, Mexico.

Other Jack Rabbits. The handsomest of the jack rabbits is Allen's Jack Rabbit, *Lepus alleni*. It has very long legs, and enormous ears, larger than those of any other hare or rabbit; they measure seven inches in total length. Its head-and-body length is two feet; its tail

THE RABBIT FARMERS HATE

The black-tailed or California jack rabbit causes more trouble than any other hare. Farmers throughout western U.S.A. hunt it relentlessly, and one Oregon county, in a single year, paid bounties for a million tails. The California jack's cousin, the white-tailed jack rabbit, or prairie hare, has been seen dancing in circles on moonlit nights.

is two and one-half inches. Its range extends from southern Arizona to Tepic, Mexico.

The most widespread and troublesome hare in the western United States is the Black-tailed Jack Rabbit, or Grey-sided Jack Rabbit, *Lepus californicus*. The black-tailed jack often builds up its numbers to enormous hordes; the county of Harney, Oregon, alone paid bounties for one million tails in one year.

There is no mistaking the black-tailed jack. Its buff-brown coat, its large ears tipped with black, and its black tail distinguish this species from all other rabbits and hares. It ranges from the State of Washington east to Nebraska and south into Mexico. An even more distinctive member of the group is the Espiritu Santo Island Jack Rabbit, which has a glossy, pure black coat.

SNOWSHOE RABBITS—THEY CHANGE THEIR COATS

The Varying Hare, or Snowshoe Rabbit, *Lepus americanus*, is well described by either name. It varies by changing from a reddish brown coat in summer to a white robe in winter. (The change is made by the calendar, not by the temperature.)

"Snowshoe" is equally appropriate as a name, especially when the snow is on the ground. The hairs on the animal's feet thicken and lengthen in winter, greatly enlarging the size of the feet and forming "snowshoes" for support on the soft snow.

As this hare walks or hops, it spreads its long toes wide. This gives them a firm grip on the ice. The creature is hardly ever slowed down, whether it is rushing over the softest snow or the most slippery ice.

The varying hare, like the rest of its family, is a vegetarian, feeding on succulent herbs and growing twigs. The daylight hours it spends mostly at home in the damp, marshy woodland. Its nest is a small depression made by its resting body in a safe place, usually overhung by shrubs and tall grasses. Through custom it uses a network of trails with a main road leading from its nest to the feeding ground. An adult weighs about five pounds, and is one and one-half feet long.

——VARYING HARES MATURE EARLY. Courtship and its battles begin in early March: it may be quite two weeks before a pair have mated. The father takes no interest in his young, which come thirty-six days later, usually about six of them in a litter. (There are from three to five litters in a season.) At birth the babies weigh about two and one-half ounces each, and are fully clothed with close brown fur, the proper garb for the time of year. They can move about as soon as they are dry; when a week old, they are out feeding themselves under their mother's watchful eye. The following year they are ready to mate.

——CYCLES OF THE VARYING HARE. These fertile little creatures have a life expectancy of about eight years, yet few live more than half that time. Often there may be five thousand of them to the square mile in their range, which extends from the northern tree limit of Canada and south in the mountains to Virginia and New Mexico. Sometimes, however, the hunter will search for them in vain throughout many parts of this area.

The varying hare, we have found, passes through cycles of great abundance and great scarcity. The reason for the scarcity can be explained, but the cause for the fast multiplication is a mystery.

Over a number of years the hares build up their numbers with increasing rapidity. When the peak has been reached, a plague will always spread with incredible speed through the thickly populated areas. The hares die by the tens of thousands. After the snow melts in the spring, their shrivelled bodies, strewn thickly over the forest floor, leave mute testimony to the relentless scourge of death that has passed through the hordes of hares.

Still, some have escaped the pestilence, and so the cycle can begin again.

OLD WORLD HARES

The European, Brown, or Eurasian Hare, *Lepus europaeus*, is the common hare of Europe, making its home in the many parts of that continent, as well as in Great Britain and the temperate regions of Asia and Asia Minor.

A big, heavy-bodied fellow, this leaper and springer is over two feet long, and has large ears, a long tail for a hare, and a curly brown coat. Since it does not encounter intense cold and long, snowy winters in its homeland, it does not turn white in winter.

The European hare is typical of the race, and frequents the open downs, moors, and grasslands. It takes readily to the water and is a good swimmer, often crossing from island to island off the coast of Scotland. It does still better on land: a full-grown hare in its prime has a top speed of forty-five miles per hour, as checked by speedometer. It can make good use of this speed, for it is a natural prey of the hunter, because of its size. It was classed as game in England long ago, by the Normans, and has ever since been protected as game.

——"MAD AS A MARCH HARE." Like their cousins in other lands, the "jack" hares fight furiously with their claws and teeth for possession of the does at the height of the mating season in March. Our old expression "mad as a March hare" owes its origin to their seemingly senseless behaviour as they leap into the air in combat.

During the breeding season, which extends throughout the summer, the doe has from three to five young, or leverets, at a time. They are born fully furred and with their eyes wide open.

The European hare lives on the surface of the ground, and its den is, as you might expect, nothing more than a depression on the ground in tall grass. Though the animal is usually silent, it will call its young to feed by uttering a low bugle call, which it repeats once or twice. On a still night you can hear it three hundred yards away.

Hares in Asia and Africa. We find relatives of the European hare in most parts of Asia and Africa. Generally speaking, they are not very different in their ways and appearance from the animals we have just been looking at, but we may single out a few species as particularly noteworthy. For example, one, the Woolly Himalayan Hare, likes to live high up. This silvery-grey creature makes its home at altitudes from ten thousand to sixteen thousand feet.

There are at least twenty-eight species of true hares native to Africa, the South African Grey Hare and the Cape Brown Hare being the commonest. The Grass Hare, *Poelagus*, a distinct genus, ranges from Uganda to the Sudan. This small-eared hare is of particular interest because it closely resembles the European rabbit, *Oryctolagus*, in its general appearance.

The Red Hare, *Promolagus*, found in central and South Africa, is another large form that should be mentioned. In addition to being rather colourful for a rabbit, it lives among the rocks, and barricades the entrance to its den with a pile of sticks. It is the least rabbit-like of the African hares.

AMERICAN COTTONTAILS AND PYGMY RABBITS

The Cottontail, Molly, or Briar Rabbit, *Sylvilagus* ("forest rabbit"), is the common rabbit of the American woods. It gets its most popular name from the white-tufted under-side of its tail. The animal is not a hare, nor, strictly speaking, is it a rabbit—but try convincing an American child of that!

The cottontail, about fifteen inches long, is small compared with hares and rabbits in general. Caring neither for the gloom of the deep forest nor the glare of the open plains, this animal chooses the border-land or brush country. Although its favourite feeding time is twilight, there are no time limitations on the cottontail's activities; it is abroad day and night. It feeds on plants, and is in disfavour among farmers because of the damage it does to crops. Millions and millions of cottontails are killed every year.

THE RABBIT THAT ISN'T ONE

The cottontail, molly, or briar rabbit, most common of all American rabbits, is not a true rabbit at all, nor even a hare! A gadabout, it is abroad both day and night. It is preyed on by most flesh-eaters, but, as it is prolific, there will always be cottontails. These animals are spread all over the United States, as well as Mexico and northern South America.

——A COURAGEOUS MOTHER. In startling contrast to its normally timid behaviour, there are times when the cottontail burns with hot fury, and justly, too.

Whenever a snake threatens her brood, the female cottontail opens the attack with marvellous courage and strategy. So quick and fast are her actions that even a large snake will turn and seek safety in flight to avoid being ripped to ribbons by claws and teeth. Still, a great number of wild cats, foxes, coyotes, weasels, raccoons, hawks, and eagles take a large annual toll of the cottontail. Though its life expectancy is two or three years, it seldom dies of old age.

Cottontails are prolific creatures. Five or six young are not unusual in a litter, and there may be three or four litters a season. Each litter has a different father. The mother is an expert at her trade. Often she prepares the nursery—a depression in the ground—a week or two before her babies come, lining it with her own fur.

The newborn infants, naked, helpless, and blind, weigh about three ounces. Ten days later their eyes are wide open; in fourteen days, though still tiny balls of fur, they are out sporting and playing tag together.

Mother Cottontail visits the nest only at night, to nurse the youngsters. When she leaves, she covers them with grass and wisps of her fur, so that her babies will be hidden from enemy eyes. But even by day she never seems to be far from the nursery; if the babies call, she comes quickly to drive off the marauder if she can. As we have seen, she is a staunch fighter.

WHERE WE FIND THEM. We find the true cottontail over practically the whole of the United States and Mexico, and south to Costa Rica and northern South America. Actually, its range extends from the Canadian border south to Patagonia, but the Central American and South American species differ considerably from the typical North American cottontail.

There are five distinct groups of North American cottontails—the Mountain Cottontail, the Eastern Cottontail, the Desert Cottontail, the Brush Cottontail, and the New England Cottontail.

More American Rabbits. Other kinds of American rabbits worthy of mention include the Forest Rabbit, the typical rabbit of Central and South America. The Swamp Rabbit and the Marsh Hare of the southeastern United States are cottontails that have left the dry land and taken to the water, a rather surprising development in the race. They swim with remarkable ease, and are as much at home in the water and the wet marshes as on dry land.

The Idaho Pygmy Rabbit, an underground dweller, is of particular interest because it is not only the smallest rabbit in the Americas but the smallest in the world (six to eleven inches long). The Mexican Pygmy Rabbit is more like a pika than a rabbit and averages about half an inch longer than the Idaho pygmy. We meet this little Mexican only on the Mexican volcanoes Popocatepetl and Iztaccihuatl, at altitudes of ten thousand to twelve thousand feet.

OLD WORLD RABBITS—INCLUDING THE ORIGINAL RABBIT

The European Rabbit, *Oryctolagus cuniculus*, is the "true" rabbit—the animal to which the name "rabbit" was originally applied. Native to central and southern Europe and North Africa, it was introduced into England at an early date, possibly by the Romans. It was from the stock of the true rabbits that American domestic rabbits were derived.

The true rabbit, in the wild, is a hardy, fast-breeding creature. Its sombre hues—it is greyish brown in colour—aid it in concealment. About sixteen or eighteen inches long, it will average about three pounds in weight; a large one will weigh up to six pounds. The animal's ears are moderately large.

In contrast to the hare, which nests on the surface, the rabbit lives in underground communal burrows, or warrens. These are connected by well-worn runways to the feeding grounds. Hundreds of rabbits may dwell together this way.

While living a community life in the warren the doe digs a separate den in the ground some distance away for breeding purposes. She lines this nursery with dry leaves or dead grass mixed with her own fur. The breeding season extends from February to September; the young come a month later—five to nine of them as a rule. Their story is much like that of the cottontails.

——THE RABBIT'S FOES. With such a high rate of reproduction, the rabbit is a serious pest. Its human and animal enemies do not find it an easy animal to destroy.

The rabbit knows full well that the best way to escape detection is to remain motionless. When caught in the open, away from a safe retreat, it will flatten itself out on the earth and "freeze". Even on a plot of bare ground it is by no means easy to detect a crouched rabbit; it will stay there until almost stepped on, and then it will spring up and race for the nearest shelter.

Mother Rabbit, like Mother Cottontail, will put up a fight to defend her young. On one occasion a gamekeeper at Tunbridge Wells, Kent, saw a stoat playing with a young rabbit just as a cat will play with a mouse it has caught. Suddenly a full-grown rabbit—probably the doe—rushed up. It sailed into the stoat, knocked it over, and made off with the young one in its mouth. Recovering itself, the stoat followed in hot pursuit, but was soon seen in a hasty retreat, chased by two adult rabbits.

Foxes and badgers are also mortal enemies of the rabbit, but the ferocious stoat is responsible for more rabbit deaths than either of these. Once on a rabbit's trail, a stoat will follow the particular individual underground. It will hound its chosen prey through a warren full of rabbits and eventually run it down, we are told. (This case, certainly, would be hard to prove.)

Apparently there are still stranger goings-on in these warrens. J. A. Millais, the British naturalist, tells of an occasion where a ferret was sent down a rabbit hole. A little while later, out came a few rabbits —a fox—a stoat—and a cat!

——A COLOURFUL RELATIVE. Like the true rabbit, most of its relatives have a sombre colour, without any characteristic markings. In Asia we do, however, meet one with a very striking colour pattern. This creature, the Sumatra Rabbit, *Nesolagus*, presents an attractive combination of greyish yellow, mahogany brown, and black. Starting at its nose, a black stripe runs the length of its body.

The Rodents—Mammals That Gnaw

A RODENT is an animal that gnaws. To most people the name suggests only rats and mice. But it describes, just as accurately, legions of other creatures—squirrels, beavers, woodchucks and marmots, prairie dogs, chipmunks, gophers, muskrats, hamsters, lemmings, porcupines, and many others whose astonishing habits we shall soon have a look at.

There are more kinds of rodents—6,400 in all—than there are members in any other order of mammals; in actual numbers they may exceed the combined total of all other mammals alive on the earth today!

WORK OF THE RODENTS

The rodents represent a mighty force in the world, and their strength lies in numbers. You may be surprised to learn that the combined efforts of these industrious creatures play an important part in making and keeping the earth habitable for us.

How do they help us? The rodents clear out excess forest growth and replant denuded areas; they contribute to the creation of vast forest areas and aid greatly in natural conservation of our water supply. Digging and burrowing, they transform barren wastes into fertile soil.

On the debit side of the ledger, rodents have been instrumental in taking the lives of more people than all the wars this world has ever known. Many rodents carry lice and fleas that are disseminators of various plagues such as typhus, trichina, infectious jaundice and numerous other serious diseases.

THE RODENTS HAVE TRAVELLED FAR

The rodents have entered most fields of animal activity and have literally covered the face of the earth from the border of the Arctic ice-fields to the last tip of dry land in the Antarctic. Somehow, rodents even bridged the impassable gulf between Australia and the mainland of Asia—a feat that all other placental land mammals, except the bats, had failed to accomplish.

Rodents have entered the water, climbed into treetops, burrowed underground; some, while not actually able to fly, have learned to volplane. Most of the smaller rodents are of the scurrying type, but there are fast runners, hoppers, and high jumpers in their ranks, as well as some that are slow-moving.

Rodents build the finest nests of any mammal, breed the fastest, and probably live the shortest lives. They are harvesters and hoarders. Vegetable matter is their food, but they are not all vegetarians; they supplement their diet with insects and other forms of animal life. One interesting mouse is credited with devoting much of its efforts to hunting scorpions.

FOOTPRINTS ON SNOW AND WET GROUND

Often you will see animal tracks in the snow or wet ground. At the far left there are footprints made by a cottontail rabbit. Next to them you see the imprint left by a bounding grey squirrel. Next is the track of a field mouse, and at the far right is the trail left by a beaver. Notice the prints of the webbed hind feet and the mark left by the broad dragging tail. All of these animals, except the rabbit, are rodents.

ALL KINDS OF RODENTS

One thing you will not find among the rodents, and that is monotony. The texture of the rodent hair varies from the soft, downy fur of the chinchilla to the barbed quills of the porcupine—yet both are rodents. The body structure of these animals varies amazingly, too.

Some of the groups of rodents are distantly related, and other than the fact that they are classified as rodents, seem to have little in common with the rest of their order (Rodentia). Others, though seemingly wide apart, are closely allied in descent. Anyone can see that the tree squirrel and the beaver are very different animals both in appearance and habits—yet the beaver is a close kin of the squirrel.

TEETH LIKE CHISELS

The chief feature by which we can tell the rodents from all other mammals is the pair of large, chisel-like incisor teeth they have at the front of both their upper and lower jaws. They use these front teeth constantly in gnawing.

Subject to severe wear, the incisors would soon be mere useless stumps if they did not continue to grow throughout life. A precious possession, they often mean the difference between living and dying to the rodent. If it damages one, it can no longer feed properly; or the opposing tooth may grow right through the bone of the other jaw and kill the creature.

The rest of the rodent's teeth are placed well back in its mouth, and a wide space separates them from the incisors. The hares and rabbits are often mistaken for rodents because they have a similar dental arrangement, but they possess another pair of teeth behind the upper incisors.

RODENTS OF TODAY AND YESTERDAY

All in all, we find that these animals fall into three main groups, or suborders. The first contains the squirrels and their relatives (Sciuromorpha), the most primitive of the rodents.

The second group is much larger—it would take a six-hundred-page book just to list the members of the 186 genera here. They include the typical rats, mice, voles, lemmings, and like creatures (Myomorpha).

The last group is the most specialized—in it we place the porcupines, guinea pigs, and their kin (Hystricomorpha). To this third division also belong such isolated curiosities as the mole rats and gundis.

Paul A. Moore—Tenn. Conservation Dept.

THE GROUND HOG IS A WARY ANIMAL

The ground hog, a large, ground-dwelling squirrel or marmot, makes its home in a burrow. If an enemy approaches, it seeks shelter underground. Normally the ground hog feeds on green vegetation, but when winter comes it retires to its den, where it sleeps away the cold months, drawing sustenance from the thick layer of fat that covers its body. *See page 268.*

THE PRAIRIE DOG

The prairie dog is another ground squirrel. It is active by day; its nights are spent in a den which is part of an extensive series of burrows beneath the plains of western North America. *See page 373.*

D. A. Spencer—U.S. Fish and Wildlife Service

MARMOT PEERING FROM ITS DEN

Hoary marmots, like the one pictured below, are quite at home high up on a mountain side. *See page 271.*

J. S. Dixon—U.S. Fish and Wildlife Service

TWO FLYING SQUIRRELS INVESTIGATE AN OLD STUMP

Of all of North America's squirrels, the flying squirrels are the only ones active at night. During the day, these large-eyed rodents remain hidden in a hole in a tree, or in a nest made of shredded bark. Flying squirrels do not actually fly, but use the furry membranes at their sides to support themselves as they glide soundlessly from a high place in the trees to one lower down.
See page 281.

[3-1]

The pika loves to bask in the warm sunlight in its craggy mountain home, but there is nothing lazy about the "little harvester". Should their carefully cut and tended grass be threatened with a sudden storm, the entire colony will work late into the night to gather in the crop. *See page 233*

[3-1A]

No more aggressive or intentionally offensive than any other hare or rabbit, the black-tailed jack rabbits seriously endanger man's crops in the western United States. In spite of the extreme measures taken to eradicate them, they build up their population to amazing proportions. *See page 241*

[3-2]

The white-tailed jack rabbit is one of the fleetest animals on the American western plains. Rabbits and hares never walk or run in the ordinary sense, but proceed by a series of leaps. A speed of 35 miles an hour in 12-foot hops is an easy average pace for this heavy-bodied hare. *See page 238*

[3-2A]

The marsh rabbit is native to the south-eastern United States. Surprisingly enough, it is as much at home in the water as it is on dry land.
See page 245

Rodents are a very ancient order—their history dates back to the beginning of the Age of Mammals. Well-formed rodents existed on the earth sixty million years ago, and at that early date they had already learned to climb, as the squirrels and so many others still do today.

Squirrels, Chipmunks, Beavers, and their Relatives—Important for Flesh and Fur

MOUNTAIN BEAVERS—NOT BEAVERS AT ALL

THE SEWELLEL, Mountain "Beaver", Boomer, or Whistler, *Aplodontia*, is the last survivor of a primitive race of rodents; it has no living relative. A short, chubby animal (it is about a foot long and has the thick, dark fur and the small eyes and ears of a burrower), it more nearly resembles a tailless muskrat than a beaver.

The sewellel is an odd little creature, and so are its names. First of all, "sewellel" is a Chinook Indian name, originally not for the animal itself but for a robe the Chinooks made from its skins. "Boomer" is the name used for this animal in Oregon, but the mountain boomer does not boom; neither does it whistle, as its other name implies.

The sewellel has been called the "silent one" since it is rarely known to utter a sound other than a singular rasping noise made by grating its teeth when angry. However, it is not mute, and is reported to utter a curious quavering note resembling that of a screech owl.

Furthermore, the sewellel is not a typical mountain animal. Its favourite haunts, above ground, are among the dense underbrush in wooded country that affords concealment and shelter from flesh-eaters on the prowl. One of the remarkable things about it is its limited range—we find it only in a narrow strip along the Pacific coast of North America, from the southern border of British Columbia to central California.

THE SEWELLEL'S "SUBWAY SYSTEM"

The sewellel lives underground in colonies. It excavates extensive tunnels in the earth, not, like the moles and gophers, to get at food in the soil but to provide an integrated "subway system" for the sewellel colony. By these "subways" the sewellel can travel in dark safety from one surface feeding ground to another.

A LITTLE-KNOWN RODENT OF THE AMERICAN WEST

The sewellel, at home along the western coast of the United States, is really not a beaver at all. It lacks the tail characteristic of that animal, and in general looks more like a muskrat. Sewellels live in colonies in the earth and travel by underground routes to reach their feeding ground on the surface.

This chubby rodent leaves all doors to the outside world wide open, for ready use. Once a sewellel has arrived at the exit to the feeding ground it wants to visit, it speeds out of the tunnel, hurriedly gathers its loot, and retreats underground to feed. The underground passageways form a virtual labyrinth with enlarged chambers here and there for storage of food.

A SAFETY-MINDED CLIMBER

All manner of succulent vegetation has an appetizing look to the sewellel. It does not limit itself to what is growing on the ground, but will even climb small shrubs to get at the choice green shoots on top. Here, as always, it is safety-minded—on the way up it will cut the branches off with its teeth a few inches out from the main stem, leaving a series of pegs as footholds for retreat.

The mother sewellel bears a litter of three to five young. They are believed to be born in June. We place the mountain beavers in a family by themselves, Aplodontidae.

SQUIRRELS OF THE TREES

The squirrel family (Sciuridae) is a very great one. It includes all tree squirrels and flying squirrels, and many animals that people do not commonly think of as squirrels at all—the squirrels that live on the ground, such as the woodchuck, marmot, chipmunk, and the prairie dog.

The tree and flying squirrels are mostly small, slender-bodied creatures, a foot in length or shorter, with bushy tails often as long again. The greater number are dwellers in the trees; for this kind of life their tails are essential equipment, as we shall soon see. Their relatives, the ground-dwelling squirrels, are bigger as a rule, but have smaller tails.

The squirrels are equally at home in the Old World and the New— we meet them in Europe, Asia, Africa, North America, and South America, but not in Australia or Madagascar.

The Tree Squirrel, *Sciurus* (the scientific name means "shadetail", and from it our word "squirrel" is derived), like the rabbit and the fox, is one of childhood's first picture-book animals. Every man, woman, and child in the civilized world is at least vaguely familiar with the squirrel, its long, bushy tail, and its habit of hoarding nuts. Its nervous movements, its rapid flight, its sudden appearances and disappearances are famous; these probably gave rise to the old Scandinavian legend that the squirrel is a messenger of the gods and carries news of what is going on in the world to animals in distant lands.

All true tree squirrels have a showy tail, and in some it is magnificent. The squirrel is proud of its graceful appendage and never forgets to keep it well groomed. But, for all its beauty, the tail is not solely used as a decorative feature; it is a vital necessity, and its purpose is to maintain and correct the balance of the animal in its daring leaps from branch to branch.

——THE INCREDIBLE JUMPER. The accuracy with which a squirrel can leap from one swaying bough to another and never fail in its estimate of the distance to be covered is miraculous. In a leap, the squirrel first fixes the direction, judges the space, and hurls itself in the air with feet extended forward, body flattened, and tail held straight out behind as a rudder to keep the course. At the end of the jump, the animal lands with its head up, ready to scamper away.

The author has never known a squirrel to miss its aim. Still, he can recall an occasion when a red squirrel made a long leap to a rotten branch and both came crashing to the ground. After regaining its dignity, the very annoyed creature soundly scolded everyone and everything that it could blame for its humiliating experience. It seemed to be unhurt otherwise.

Not all squirrels climb trees in exactly the same manner, but, in general, squirrels go up at a gallop, the fore and hind feet being used in pairs alternately. Coming down, the squirrel travels head first and is more careful as it moves, setting its feet individually.

——A CAREFUL HOARDER. The tree squirrels are active by day. They are habitual hoarders of nuts, seeds, fruits, and other types of vegetable food. Often they have a number of storage places, making their caches in holes in trees or underground, or next to logs or rocks. To conserve storage space, they usually shell the nuts and take the seeds and the corn from the husks. Edible mushrooms and toadstools are first sun-dried and cured in the fork of a tree before storage.

The squirrel appears to find its way back to its cache by memory, but it also has a keen sense of smell. Some of its hidden food it never locates again; it is a great planter without knowing it.

An individual pair of squirrels usually have their own particular section of woods, an area of about two hundred square yards, which they defend with vigour from thieving and enterprising neighbours.

——BABY SQUIRRELS. In the northern temperate and cold regions, many squirrels sleep, but do not truly hibernate, during the severest part of the winter. They usually mate about February; the young are born in March or April. A typical nursery, that of the grey squirrel, is the winter den—a hollow tree will serve if there is one available.

At first the young are furless, sightless, and helpless; it is five weeks before their eyes open and they are fully clothed. Once they gain their sight, the young squirrels are soon out enjoying the spring sunlight.

By the time they are old enough to eat solid food, they must vacate the den, for squirrels are not the tidiest of housekeepers. Now an airier, more sanitary home is built—a summer nest of dried leaves in the forked branch of a tree.

Tree squirrels are spread over the world in a rather surprising pattern. They are perhaps best represented in Central America and Mexico; the rest of North America is a good second. South America has a fair share of tree squirrels, but Russia, Siberia, and most of Europe have but a single species, the so-called European red squirrel.

TREE SQUIRRELS OF EUROPE AND NORTHERN ASIA

The European Red Squirrel, *Sciurus vulgaris,* is a dweller in the pine trees and evergreen forests. Though not arrayed in gaudy colours, this little fellow is one of the most attractive of all squirrels. Long tufts on the tip of its erect ears and a thick, bushy tail curled up gracefully over the back add accents of elegance to its spruce, well-groomed appearance.

The red squirrel is one of the very few really wild creatures that the casual observer may still see in the European woodlands. The gleam of its red coat (the colour commonest in Europe) as it streaks through the gloom of the evergreen trees relieves the monotony of the ever-increasing stillness of the forests. Its brilliant little eyes glitter in the sunlight while it leaps and bounds from branch to branch. It is fascinating and delightful to watch this comely, small red-furred squirrel frolicking and playing with the falling autumn leaves.

——IT CHANGES ITS COAT. The red squirrel is deceptive in appearance when seen in the treetops, giving the impression of being considerably larger than it really is. The head-and-body length is not more than about eight inches for a large male, and the female is only six and one-half inches. The superb bushy tail is seven inches long in both sexes.

In Europe, the animal's colour varies with the seasons. In October it puts on a long winter coat of greyish brown. In May the full, lengthy dress is shed and in its place grows a shorter and redder coat, but the extensive ear tufts remain until they are renewed in the autumn.

———FIGHTING FOR A MATE. The European red squirrel mates early in the year, about March. This is a time of great activity. The males fight like gamecocks. Often, locked in each other's embrace, they fall biting and scratching to the ground and roll over and over in their fury. But in a moment they separate and both go scampering after the fleeing female.

———HOW THE BABIES ARE LOOKED AFTER. Both male and female take part in building the drey, or nest, which is composed of sticks and moss and is lined with shredded bark. The drey, usually placed high up in the small top branches of a tree, looks something like a crow's nest, but it is roofed over and has an entrance on the side.

There are usually about three or four babies in a litter, born a month or so after mating time. They are naked, blind, and quite dependent at first. The red squirrel makes a good mother. When her babies' safety is threatened, she gets highly excited. One at a time she bears them away, as a cat carries her kittens, to a safer nest in a nearby tree.

———A HOARDER, BUT A WASTER, TOO. The red squirrel greedily eats beechnuts, chestnuts, hazelnuts, mushrooms and seeds of pine cones. It also cuts and eats flowers. In true squirrel fashion it sits up on its hind legs holding the kernel of a nut in its fore paws.

Unfortunately, this likeable animal is not quite without fault. It loves birds' eggs and in the spring it robs birds' nests and even eats their young. This extremely wasteful creature will scatter a whole treeful of nuts, taking scarcely a nibble out of each. In October and November the pine squirrel fills its storehouse with ripe nuts and seeds and sun-dried mushrooms, in preparation for the barren winter.

This squirrel is not out of place in the water—it can swim several hundred yards without tiring. Wisely, it prefers to cross a stream the easy way over a bridge.

The only representative of the squirrel family in Europe and northern Asia, the red squirrel is spread over the forestlands from the Atlantic coast of Europe east to the Pacific coast of Siberia. Other tree-dwelling squirrels occur in the same area as the red squirrel, but are not true tree squirrels. Africa has tree squirrels, but no typical ones.

The forty varieties of the species, adapted for varying kinds of climate, range in coat colour from the subdued red type common in Europe to the black pelage flecked with white typical in eastern Siberia. Only one typical species, the Iranian Tree Squirrel, is found in southern Asia. Though not very different in general from its European cousin, it is bright yellowish red and lacks the attractive ear tufts.

——HUNTING THE SQUIRREL. Squirrel hunting was once a common practice in England and on the continent of Europe. It used to be the custom to fell the animals with sticks weighted at one end. While the pelt of the red squirrel is not valued by the fur trade for wearing apparel, it was traditional for the Scots to wear red squirrel on the occasion of marriage. The black Siberian pelts were popular in the fur trade until the enforcement of restrictions on the fur trade with Russia.

——FOLK TALES ABOUT THE SQUIRREL. As might be expected, the little redcoat bobs up in many different chapters of European folklore. In Germany people used to believe there was an alliance between the squirrels (the little people of the trees) and the elves of the grass and flowers. For its bright red coat, Norse mythology associated the red squirrel with the great god Thor. The Edda places this excellent climber in the biggest tree of all—the ash tree Ygdrasil, whose branches embrace the world. On top, it relates, sat an eagle and among the roots dwelt a serpent. Between the two the squirrel ran up and down, seeking to sow the seeds of dissension.

NORTH AMERICA'S TREE SQUIRRELS

The American Red Squirrel, *Sciurus* (*Tamiasciurus*) *hudsonicus*, is the noisiest and most rollicking creature in the northern evergreen forests; it is always ready to chatter and scold at any stranger that passes along. It can utter a seething monologue of rage, often sputtering, stamping its feet, and jerking its tail in fury. When not disturbed, it also has a long, vibrant, rolling call, which may be answered by another red squirrel in the distance. These vocal accomplishments have tagged it with such names as chickaree, boomer, and barking squirrel.

——THE SQUIRREL'S HOARD. The red squirrel is on the move during daylight hours throughout the year; one sees it about during the coldest days of winter. It feeds largely on the seeds from pine and spruce cones. When the seeds are ripe in the autumn, it busily harvests large quantities and then carries them to a carefully guarded store-house, along with mushrooms and toadstools which it has first sun-dried and cured.

The American red squirrel is charged with occasionally robbing a bird's nest—and has been caught in the act—but there are no other black marks against its name.

——AVOIDING ENEMIES. The home territory of one of these little rodents covers an area of about two hundred square yards. By and large, in the evergreen forests, the average population is about one squirrel to each four acres; but the number will vary with the abundance of food. The range of these animals extends from the forestlands of Labrador to Alaska and south into the eastern United States to Pennsylvania and Tennessee.

Through custom, the squirrel knows every branch and tree in its restricted domain and will fight any intruding squirrel that dares to trespass upon it. It not only has a domicile in a tree, but also a labyrinth of underground tunnels and runways in which to elude pursuers such as hawks, owls, and martens.

In its own territory, the squirrel can easily outmanoeuvre its arch-enemy, the marten; but once the marten succeeds in edging it off its home ground, there is one squirrel less. The red squirrel may live to the grand old age of ten years, yet it begins to show signs of decline after its fifth year.

——MOTHERS AND BABIES. American red squirrels mate in the early spring, beginning about February; the height of the season is in March. The mother-to-be prepares a bulky nest among the branches of a tree or simply settles in a hollow tree trunk. About forty days after mating, she bears from two to six young, in a comparatively immature state.

Although in a few days a downy fur appears on their bodies, the babies do not open their eyes until about the twenty-seventh day, and they are not able to care for themselves until fully five weeks old.

They can count on their mother to nurse them and watch over them up to this age and longer.

In winter the pert little squirrel displays a broad rusty-red band down its back, contrasting with its olive-grey body colour and white under-parts; in summer a black stripe appears on its sides. Its head-and-body length is six and one-half inches, and the tail is about an inch shorter.

——OTHER RED SQUIRRELS. The Chickaree replaces the red squirrel in the evergreen forests west of the Rocky Mountains. It is very similar to its more northern cousin, but has no rusty-red band on its back, and is reddish brown instead of white underneath. Fremont's Pine Squirrel is like the chickaree except for white under-parts and a white fringe to its tail. It is found in southern Wyoming and in the southern Rocky Mountain states.

The Grey Squirrel, *Sciurus carolinensis*, is a familiar figure in eastern North America and in Europe. It is a resident of groves of oak, maple, chestnut, and hickory trees from the Atlantic Ocean to the Great Plains and from southern Canada to the Gulf region of the United States. In England it is rapidly ousting the red squirrel; in many areas the red squirrel is no longer to be seen.

——STRANGE SQUIRREL MIGRATIONS. Up to comparatively recent times, the grey squirrel engaged in curious, inexplicable migrations. When its numbers reached their peak in one region, some unknown influence would urge them to move out.

At first, the migrants would be a comparatively small group, but as the company moved along, others would join up and the army increased rapidly. Two such armies, actuated by the same impulse, would join forces, and the combined legions would be joined by still other marching hordes.

The stories of such migrations told by pioneers and homesteaders of a hundred years ago seem almost incredible. According to these accounts, the great grey squirrel migrations recruited armies a hundred thousand strong. They seemed possessed with an unswerving desire to travel in a straight line.

What the strange attraction was at that point of the compass toward which the squirrels headed, no one will ever know. But on they went. They crossed open prairies, climbed precipitous mountain crags, and swam roaring torrents. The bodies of hundreds of dead squirrels strewed the countryside or floated in streams, grim testimonials to the determination of the travellers.

——OLD SQUIRREL TRADITION REVIVES. These mass migrations are a thing of the past, but old squirrel "tradition" revives. In the autumn of 1933, the squirrels in eastern Connecticut seemed to be up to something. Upon investigation, the author found that a thousand grey squirrels had already swum across the Connecticut River on 24 September. Seventy-five were counted crossing a lake, and another indefinite number were seen moving in the same direction.

A FAMOUS TREE SQUIRREL

The grey squirrel is a well-known animal throughout Britain and the eastern half of the United States. Generally it is grey in colour, but black "grey" squirrels are seen in some places. These animals are extraordinary leapers, and balance themselves in the air with the help of their large, bushy tails.

They reached the Hudson River on 10 December. Hundreds crossed the Bear Mountain Bridge, but the majority swam the Hudson. A few boldly marched on board the ferry boats at Yonkers, New York, and stole a ride across the river. Once on the New Jersey side of the river, they scampered ashore. Here all traces of the army were lost.

——TANGLED TAILS. The grey squirrels have other curious habits. Not the least remarkable is that on occasion they tangle their tails. Unable to separate them and escape, the animals may starve to death.

In December, 1951, a keeper at the New York Zoological Park noticed no fewer than seven squirrels huddled together in the Park grounds. Their bodies were extended in all directions but bound together by their tails. The hair of the tails was so twisted and interwoven that it had to be cut away in order to separate the animals. All were adult; two females were dead and another soon died; four recovered and were released.

——HUNTING THE GREY SQUIRREL. Grey squirrel hunting has always been a popular sport with the country boy. The squirrel is well aware when the hunting season opens, and it is no easy matter to pick one off with a .22 rifle in a leafy oak tree. Flattening itself on a thick branch, the rodent slides around to the opposite side as fast as the hunter moves to get a better view. Always the animal tries to keep the branch in between itself and the hunter. Should it fail, it makes a tasty dish, which is often served in the eastern states.

The grey squirrel mates late in the winter, about January or February. The nursery is usually built of dry leaves and twigs in the protected shelter of a hollow tree. After a period of forty-four days the young are born. Their life is much like that of the red squirrel. They are not fully grown until about two years old, although they may breed at one year of age.

——EASTERN AND WESTERN GREY SQUIRRELS. The eastern grey squirrel is a large squirrel with a head-and-body length of nine inches. Pepper-and-salt grey is its normal colour, but it has a strong tendency to become black in some localities. Its life expectancy is not more than ten years, but few ever reach this age under natural conditions. In captivity, the grey squirrel may live for fifteen years.

The Western Grey Squirrel, *Sciurus griseus*, of the Pacific Coast region of the United States, is quite distinct from its eastern cousin. It is grey in colour but larger, and with a handsomer tail and longer and finer fur.

The Tufted-eared or Tassel-eared Squirrel, *Sciurus aberti*, is a big, handsome, heavy-bodied fellow noteworthy for the elegant tall black tufts of hair that rise from its long ears. Its dwelling place is the great belt of yellow pine trees that stretches in a narrow strip along the Rocky Mountains from the southern United States to Mexico.

Naturalists distinguish three different but closely related forms of the tufted-ear—the Abert, Kaibab, and Durango squirrels. Among the gaudiest of the tree squirrels, they vary in colour in certain regions. Still, their basic pattern is much the same: a soft lead-grey colour, broken by a reddish-brown saddle, spreads over the back, while a coal-black line on the side sets off the snow-white under-parts. The tail is large and bushy, with a graceful arch to it.

The tufted-eared squirrel usually builds a bulky nest of twigs and pine needles in the top of a great tree. It makes the nest about the size of a bushel basket and lines it with soft, shredded bark. From the outside it is a rough-looking, dome-shaped structure. But it is securely woven into the tree's branches, and is strong enough to resist high winds and winter storms. In it the tufted-ear remains day after day when the weather is not to its liking, venturing out only for food.

The tufted-eared squirrel does not store up a supply of nuts and seeds for winter food, but depends largely on the bark of the yellow pines in which it lives. (In summer, though, it feeds on much the same fare that other tree squirrels do.)

When the snow starts to melt in the Rockies, this handsome squirrel begins to lose the heavy winter coat it grew in the autumn, but the stately plumes on its ears, one and one-half inches long, are retained until early in June. These grow back again, however, in time for the next winter.

Families of three or four baby tufted-eared squirrels arrive early in June. (It is possible there is a second litter which is born around September.) They are weaned on the inner bark of the tall straight pine trees and are taught to seek mushrooms, birds' nests, seeds and edible roots. Soon they are scampering about in the trees and chattering furiously with their elders. Under the protection of the United States Forest Service, the tribe leads a life of security in the Grand Canyon National Park, but in the wild forests of the American South-west and northern Mexico it is cautious and wary of hunters.

Fully grown, the tufted-eared squirrel is about twenty inches long, and weighs up to two pounds.

The Fox Squirrel, *Sciurus niger,* is the largest tree squirrel in eastern North America. It resembles the common grey squirrel in general appearance, but you can tell this one apart by its larger size and orange or brownish grizzled coat. It owes its name to its great, fox-like face.

If you are to see the fox squirrel at all, it will be in scattered localities in the eastern half of the United States; the animal is quite scarce nowadays. Usually it favours open upland groves of oak, hickory, and beech trees rather than the deep, unbroken forest. In the South it will be found in the cypress swamps and long-leaf pines. Because of its large size, it is not particularly nimble in the trees, though it is a fairly fast and graceful runner on the ground. Several fox squirrels may haunt the same wooded area, but they pay scant attention to each other. Old males stick strictly to themselves.

——A LATE RISER. Squirrels in general are early risers, but not the fox squirrel; on cold, frosty mornings it will "lie in bed" till noon. Its den, most often, is in a tree, and the floor of the chamber is covered with pieces of bark and dry leaves. In the summer it may weave a number of large nests of leaves and twigs; it is a frequent mover. In winter it builds more carefully, and makes a solid, durable dwelling.

A hoarder by instinct, the fox squirrel caches nuts fast and furiously in little holes in the ground. It is also an eater of insects, bark, berries, sap, and seeds.

——MATING AND MOTHERHOOD. The mating period begins in January, when the males utter an often-repeated low bark. About a month and a half after mating time, the young are born, generally in a hollow tree trunk or a leaf nest their mother has built. Up to five in number, at birth the babies are naked, pinkish little bundles of helplessness, weighing less than an ounce each. In two weeks they are clothed with the lightest beginnings of a fur coat but their eyes will not be open for a month yet. They stay babies for a long time.

Fortunately, the infants can rely on their mother's tender care. If she has to move from the nest, she carries her brood with her, taking them one at a time and holding them with her teeth. When eight weeks old, they are able to eat solid food and on about the seventieth day can crack nuts; it is not long after this that they set out to make their own way in the world.

There is some evidence that fox squirrels may pair for life. We do know that pairs frequently live together in some particular hollow tree for a number of successive years. When the time comes to rear the family, the male behaves like many of our old-fashioned fathers—he retires to a nearby solitary residence and does not return until the young have been weaned.

A full-grown fox squirrel weighs about two pounds and is roughly two feet long. Its average life is about six or seven years, but this is sometimes shortened by its enemies, the hawks, owls, foxes, raccoons, and man.

COLOURFUL TREE SQUIRRELS OF SOUTH AND CENTRAL AMERICA

The rest of the world has its tree squirrels, and has them in plenty. We find a surprisingly large number of showy ones in Mexico and Central America. Especially interesting is the Fire-bellied Squirrel of Mexico, so named because it is bright red below, contrasting with the pale grey colour of the back. The Canyon and Apache Squirrels are well-known Mexican species allied to the fox squirrels of farther north.

The Variegated Squirrel is perhaps the best known and the most widely spread of Central America's larger squirrels. It shows a remarkable variation in colour pattern; its hues range with the locality, from almost white through combinations of bright red, buffy, yellow, brown to entirely black. Closely related, but smaller and less spectacular, is Humboldt's Squirrel, an olive-grey creature with a wide range in Central and South America.

Flame Squirrels. The Flame Squirrels of South America are a flashy group of variously coloured species. The name was first applied to one kind with fur of such brilliant red hue that it suggests a tongue of flame as it leaps through the dark tropical forests.

Pygmy Squirrels. In most groups of animals there is a pygmy and the American squirrels are no exception. In fact there are two midget squirrels there. The Common Pygmy Squirrel, *Microsciurus*, is widely distributed in the Andes of South America and north to Nicaragua. The Midget Squirrel, *Sciurillus*, is even smaller, having a head-and-body length of four and one-half inches. It is unique because it is not closely related to any of the American squirrels; its range is the Lower Amazon and Guiana region.

(However, the distinction of being the smallest squirrel in the world goes to a tiny little creature, *Nannosciurus*, two and a half to three inches long with a tail of equal length, found on the islands of the South Pacific. There are several species but none is much larger than a mouse.)

TREE SQUIRRELS OF ORIENTAL ASIA AND THE PACIFIC ISLANDS

The Indian Palm Squirrel, *Funambulus*, is the favourite squirrel of India. It is easily recognized by its small size and the three white lines that run down the back from the neck to the rump.

The Indian palm squirrel is commonly found in groves and gardens and often enters dwelling houses; though occasionally seen in palm trees, it is by no means partial to them.

In movement, this squirrel is quick and jerky. It is extremely agile in the trees, making astonishing leaps from branch to branch, often covering a distance of five feet or more. Well aware of the fact that when chased it is not safe in a small tree, at the first opportunity it will make for a larger one. The female has from two to four young in a bulky nest of twigs and grass built in the branches of a tree.

The palm squirrel eats nuts, seeds and fruits and is frequently seen on the ground feeding in company with parties of birds called Babblers. The squirrels and birds are apparently on the best of terms. Interestingly enough, the animal's cry is shrill and birdlike.

The palm squirrel is easily tamed and makes a very pleasing pet. Its attractive habit of sitting up when feeding, with a morsel of food held between the forepaws, and its lively and confiding ways make it most popular with the natives of India and Ceylon.

The Oriental Giant Squirrel, *Ratufa*, is a Goliath among the squirrels—it is the largest tree squirrel in Asia. Some species have a total length of over three feet.

The giant squirrel or "tree dog" is about only during the day and inhabits tall trees in heavy jungles. It is most active from dawn until about nine in the morning, and from four in the afternoon until dusk. It is exceedingly fast and agile. When alarmed, it makes off through the tree-tops with almost unbelievable rapidity—it can easily cover twenty feet in one leap from tree to tree.

During the heat of the day the Oriental giant rests lazily in a nest built in the small branches and foliage of a tall tree. The animal usually has several such nests, lined with green leaves: the natives claim that it always builds seven. Not a sociable creature, it lives either singly or in pairs. Its call is a startling, loud, shrill cackle, often repeated in the early morning.

We know little about the breeding habits of the giant squirrel. Usually there appears to be only one baby in a litter. Taken at an early stage, the young are easily raised and make entertaining pets. One lived sixteen years in captivity.

Second Only to the Rat in Numbers. Among the many other kinds of Asiatic squirrels the Common Oriental Squirrel, *Callosciurus*, is especially noteworthy because it has the largest number of squirrel species and the most variable ones. There are approximately 320 forms already named—this squirrel is second in number of different kinds of animals in any genus, the common rat being first. Some of the Orientals are striped, others have red bellies and many combinations and shades of colours.

Prevost's Tree Squirrel, from Malacca, is the most distinctive and ornate of the entire group. There is no doubt that this particular squirrel suggested the name *Callosciurus*, which means "beautiful squirrel". It is black above, deep chestnut below with white bands from the cheeks to the hips.

AFRICA'S TREE SQUIRRELS

Even though Africa is separated from the rest of the world by vast expanses of water and arid, treeless deserts, it has its own particular kinds of tree squirrels. Spread over the entire continent, they vary from large to tiny in size. A few are marked with ornamental stripes like the American chipmunks, but most are coloured in conservative shades of red, grey, and buff

The Oil Palm Squirrel, *Protoxerus*, is known as the giant squirrel of Africa. Over a foot in length, it has a bushy tail even longer. This creature is remarkable because for some unexplainable reason the under-side of the body is almost naked.

Quite a contrast to this animal is provided by the Pygmy Squirrel,

[3-3]

Largest of all hares, the Arctic hare makes its home in the barren wastelands near the northern icecap. Grey or brown during the short summer, with the coming of winter it moults the dark coat in favour of a pure white one. *See page 237*

[3-3A]

Rabbits and hares have been around for some 30 million years and we seldom bother to make the fine distinction between the two. The snowshoe rabbit, or varying hare (it is a hare), also changes its coat with the seasons. In winter the hair on its feet grows longer and thicker, actually providing the animal with snowshoes.
See page 241

[3-4]

The cottontail is small compared with either hares or rabbits.
With five or six young in a litter and three or four litters a
season, the species flourishes even though millions are killed
each year by hunters and justifiably irate farmers.

See page 244

[3-5]

This small round animal is the last survivor of a primitive race of rodents and with no living relatives is in a family all by itself. Mountain beaver, sewellel, boomer, whistler, silent-one: none of its common names apply.
See page 251

[3-5A]

Noisiest of all mammals in the North American evergreen forests, the American red squirrel stakes out a "homestead" and defends it with scolding chatter or actual battle depending upon the intruder. While it feeds mainly on seeds from pine cones, the squirrel also gathers and dries mushrooms and toadstools for its winter hoard.
See page 257

[3-6]

The long bushy tail of the grey squirrel is sometimes a hazard as well as a beautiful, useful appendage—two or more of the animals will get their tails entangled and, unable to separate them, starve to death. *See page 259*

[3-6A]

The fox squirrel, largest of North American tree squirrels, is more adept on the ground than in the trees. In summer it will move from one leafy nest to another, but in winter it makes a snug, substantial den where it lies in bed until noon. *See page 263*

Myosciurus ("mouse squirrel"), of West Africa. With a head-and-body length of only three inches and a tail even shorter, it is the smallest squirrel on the Dark Continent. It is also of interest because there is only a single species, which does not vary throughout its range.

The "Sun Squirrel". The Isindi, *Heliosciurus* ("sun squirrel"), is almost as large as the oil palm squirrel, but is found in more places and is better known: there are forty-seven varieties that range from coast to coast in Equatorial Africa. The animal's scientific name was derived from its habit of basking in the tropical sun on the branches of trees; this also explains why its fur is often sun-bleached and faded.

The Tree Squirrel that Likes the Ground. Not all African tree squirrels spend their time exclusively in the trees. The Bush Squirrel, *Paraxerus*, for example, often hunts on the ground. This rodent is extremely variable, not only in size but in colour and colour pattern. An East and South African squirrel, it may be either striped, white sided, red bellied or just plain olive brown.

GROUND-DWELLING SQUIRRELS

WOODCHUCKS AND MARMOTS

The large, heavy-bodied animals known as marmots—the American species are called woodchucks or ground hogs—are ground-dwelling squirrels. Too big and clumsy to climb trees, they live in burrows in the ground or have their dens among rocks. You will see them up and doing only in broad daylight during the summer months. Loving a life of comfort and ease, they sleep all night, and all winter, too.

The Marmot's Long Winter Sleep. When summer has gone, but before the air is chilled with the autumn frost, the marmot retreats to its deep winter den. It will not see the light of day again until the spring sunshine warms the earth. It packs a relatively small cache of green fodder into the underground chambers. Then it plugs all entrances to the burrow securely, with a foot or more of earth mixed with straw. Usually two to four marmots hibernate together, but as many as fourteen have been found in one winter den.

At the start of its long, continuous winter sleep, the marmot's breathing slackens and its body temperature drops, until a state of lethargy has been reached. The body temperature of a hibernating marmot ranges from 43° to 57° Fahrenheit; at this time the animal is insensible and to all appearances dead. It would take several hours in a warm room to awaken it from its winter sleep.

"Ground-Hog Day". American tradition has it that on the second day of February the ground hog comes out of its den for the first time in the year. If the sun is shining and the animal sees its own shadow, it will retreat underground for another six weeks of slumber. Accordingly, the forecast is for continued cold and a late spring. If the day is cloudy and the ground hog fails to see its shadow, it is a sign that the cold weather is over and there will be an early spring.

——TRUE OR FALSE? What is the truth of this tradition? Although the ground hog is not the most reliable of weather prophets, clear skies in February often come with cold weather; cloudy days usually are warm at this season of the year.

The source of the superstition of Ground-Hog Day is not known. It is generally supposed to have originated among Negroes of the middle-eastern states, but the legend of Ground-Hog Day is actually a remarkable example of the transfer of Old World folklore to the New World. In Europe the second of February is associated with Candlemas Day, but in this instance the hedgehog and the badger play the role of weather prophet.

Where We Find the Marmot. Despite its love of warmth and its dread of cold, the marmot does not live in tropical countries, and none has crossed the Equator. In fact, it favours the temperate regions of the Northern Hemisphere. Most of the United States and Canada is marmot or woodchuck country. In the Old World these rodents are found in the Alps of Europe, and eastward in the mountains to China and north-eastern Siberia.

The Woodchuck, or Ground Hog, *Marmota monax*, is common in the eastern United States. The smallest of the American marmots, it weighs eight or nine pounds. In the autumn, however, when it is fat, it may weigh up to fourteen. When the woodchuck comes out in the spring, it is almost as fat as it was in the autumn but soon loses its stored reserve; by April, the animal is quite lean.

——BABY MARMOTS. Mating begins in March, when the woodchuck comes out of hibernation. Four or five one-ounce baby chucks are born a month later. At first they are quite naked and sightless. It is a month before they open their eyes, but they are then fully clothed and ready to scramble on their shaky legs to get their first view of the outside world.

The young increase their weight to about three pounds by August and are big enough to take care of themselves. They then leave home and seek their own fortune. This, on the whole, amounts to digging a den and getting fat.

THE ANIMAL AFTER WHICH A DAY IS NAMED

Every American schoolchild knows that 2 February is Ground-Hog Day. The American marmot or woodchuck, better known as the ground hog, is considered a weather prophet—if it emerges from its burrow on the second day of February and sees its shadow, a long winter is predicted. Often this forecast turns out to be correct.

——THE WOODCHUCK'S HOME. The woodchuck usually provides its burrow with a nest chamber and several side rooms. It likes to have three "doorways" to the outside world. First there is the "front door", with a pile of dirt at the opening. A "back door" is hidden in the bushes as an emergency exit. The third opening is a drop hole that has no tell-tale soil around it and goes straight down for two feet or more.

When an intruder approaches, the chuck will sit confidently on the

270 SQUIRRELS, BEAVERS, AND THEIR RELATIVES

edge of the drop hole to the last safe moment, then suddenly drop out of sight down the two-foot shaft to the runway below.

The woodchuck is fastidious about sanitary conditions. When conditions are not favourable outside, it uses one of its side rooms as a toilet and covers its faeces with soil. In fair weather an outside mound of earth is used, generally the pile of loose earth at the main entrance.

Every spring the chuck remodels and improves its castle in the ground. New rooms are excavated, old ones enlarged and renovated, and piles of fresh earth are shovelled out at the main entrance of the den.

For some unexplainable reason the animal reverts to the proverbial squirrel habit of filling its storehouse with food in the autumn. On several occasions the author has found caches of green grass packed in the side tunnels of the woodchuck's den. In some of the pockets the grass was mouldy or mildewed and quite inedible.

——A Lazy Life. The woodchuck's life is one we might well envy. While the day is still young—but not too early in the morning—the chuck is out feasting on the fresh, tender leaves of grass, clover, and other sweet, green vegetation. When the sun rises high overhead the chuck, its belly now full, stretches out lazily on the shady side of some cool rock or under a leafy tree. As the shadows begin to lengthen in the afternoon, the animal feasts once more. At sundown it retires to the seclusion of its warm nest for a night's sound slumber.

On one occasion the author surprised a woodchuck fast asleep on a warm, sunny hillside. It would be hard to say which of us was the more startled. With a whistle the animal suddenly sprang up and bolted through the briars, making as much noise as a dozen animals its size.

While the chuck is too fat and lazy to climb, it can scramble up a tree trunk. It rarely ascends higher than the first fork; one observer, however, reports seeing a chuck fifty feet up in a tree.

——Where We Find It. In the United States, we find the eastern woodchuck is found from the Atlantic coast west to the Mississippi Valley, with the exception of the Gulf States. Its range stretches across the continent in Canada and extends north to Alaska. When this creature is fully grown, its broad head and chubby body are about twenty inches long. Its limbs are short, and so is its flat tail. The fur, moderately long and coarse, is brownish grey in colour.

Another species, the Yellow-bellied Marmot, or Rock Chuck, lives in the American West.

The Hoary Marmot, or Whistler, *Marmota caligata*, keeps strict watch over its home territory in the high mountains of north-western America and north-eastern Siberia. Whenever a stranger enters its realm, this big marmot sounds a danger signal—a shrill, high-pitched whistle that can be heard a mile away.

Seemingly, there is always a sentinel like this, "posted" on a high rock to keep watch and give warning. (Probably no marmot in particular is the sentry—any one will give the signal.) It is needed, for the hoary marmot is definitely social; the little communities of half a dozen or more use the same trails and retreats, and their enemies know it. Fortunately, the marmots also have far-reaching eyesight, as do most creatures that live high up in the mountains, and are constantly watching for the prowling bear, the hungry wolverine, and the fisher that may come along at any hour.

These are about the only animals that could kill an adult marmot. A golden eagle will take the young and probably could kill a full-grown marmot caught unawares. The marmot, however, is always ready for an emergency. No matter how far it seems to wander in search of the grass, flowers, and succulent plants on which it feeds, it is never too far away from a drop hole into which it can plunge as soon as it hears the alarm.

——THE HOARY MARMOT'S WHISTLE. The marmot's sharp whistle is not made with its lips, but seems to be formed in the throat; the mouth is not open nor do the lips move when the sound peals out. It has a piercing quality, especially clear in the rarefied air, far above the timber line, in the hoary marmot's northern home.

Here, toiling up the steep, trailless slopes of the Mackenzie Range and the mountains of subarctic America, the author has seen, moving about in a silent summer paradise, small bands of caribou and white mountain sheep, solitary moose, climbing goats, and an occasional bear; but the only sound that ever broke the universal quiet was the shrill call of the great marmot, perched high up on some outstanding rocky crag.

——PROFOUND SLEEPERS. In the rocky wastes of the North-west, you can hear this call for a brief season and no more. The winter is long, the spring break-up comes late and snow begins to fall again as early as August. The marmots in these remote outposts of Nature are conscious for only three months out of the year. The other nine months they spend in profound sleep.

The hoary marmot weighs up to twenty pounds; it will stand seven inches at the shoulders. It measures about thirty inches from its snout to the tip of the eight-inch tail. Its fur, used by the Eskimos for making robes, is grizzled, with some mixture of reddish brown. White-tipped hairs frost the coat, and give the animal its name.

Other Well-known Marmots. The European or Alpine Marmot, *Marmota marmota*, a greyish-brown creature much like the American breed, is still found in the Alps and ranges east into the mountains of Asia. Tradition would persuade us that this marmot uses a living wagon to transport hay to its den.

——A TALL TALE. According to such ancient nature historians as Pliny, Topsell, and Gesner, the European marmots gather a great quantity of hay. Now one of them lies down on its back, lifting its feet toward heaven, and the hay is loaded on the animal's belly and kept in place by the four limbs. Next, the other marmots take the supine one's tail in their mouths and drag their brother home like a sledge. As each takes a turn of service as a wagon some time or other, none has any hair on its back at this season of the year.

Topsell, however, concludes his account with this telling sentence: "I cannot affirm certainly whether this be a truth or a falsehood . . . but that some of them have been found bald on the back." A like tale is told about the rat.

——CHINESE AND KASHMIR MARMOTS. The Chinese Marmot, or Bobac as it is often called in China, is much hunted for its fur, which is used as a counterfeit marten. The creature is protected during the mating season by the Chinese but dug from the burrows at other times. It comes out of hibernation in the spring carrying a heavy coat of fat which it quickly loses. The Mongols of the Central Asian steppes are fond of this fat and hunt the animal for food when it first appears. Marmots are clean feeders and wholesome to eat.

The Red Marmot of Kashmir is one of the several other Asiatic marmots. It differs from all others not only in having a rusty-red coat and black back but also in having an unusually long tail for a marmot—about half the length of the head and body.

PRAIRIE DOGS—AND THEIR DOG TOWNS

The Prairie Dog, *Cynomys* ("dog mouse"), of the midwestern United States, is not a dog but a ground squirrel. A fat little bob-tailed rodent, it was as much a part of the Old West as the Indian and the buffalo. Like the others, it has all but vanished. It did not fall before the guns of the frontiersmen; the cattlemen killed it off with strychnine, for it fed on the forage they needed for their herds.

In early pioneer days, the prairie dogs were famous for their "towns". These were actual underground cities, with miles and miles of well-worn tunnels and dens extending in every direction beneath plateaus and upland prairies. The horde of individuals in a big town was almost incalculable; a large one may have had millions. A few towns still persist in out-of-the-way places, but their numbers are limited.

Protecting the Entrances. Town building requires considerable skill; moreover, these industrious little animals must work constantly to keep them in repair. Mounds of earth are built high around the entrances to ensure the safety of the home and to prevent flooding, a most serious menace to animals that live underground.

A Prairie Dog Secret. One of the riddles still to be solved about the dog town is how these resourceful creatures excavate the soil as they extend their burrows.

The entrance hole goes almost vertically down, ten or twelve feet, before it levels off to a horizontal subway. The prairie dog could hardly scratch the soil out behind it or push it up on its head and it cannot carry such a load in its arms or mouth. Yet somehow it does get a large pile of soil up this perpendicular chute.

Prairie Dog Lynchings. There are many strange stories told about the prairie dog. For example, it is reported that when one of their members has in some way transgressed community laws, a mob of dogs has lynched the offender; this practice of ganging together and putting some individual to death has been recorded more than once. Prairie dogs apparently bury their dead and they will cover up and bury any other small animal that dies in a dog town.

When Enemies Approach the Dog Town. The fat prairie dogs are hunted by badgers, coyotes, foxes, ferrets, and wild cats. Eagles and hawks swoop down to grab them from the air.

Rattlesnakes and small burrowing owls sometimes take up residence with the prairie dogs in their towns, but it must not be supposed they are really their friends or anybody's. Each of these predators will devour the other's offspring, and a baby prairie dog is a juicy morsel for them. It has been claimed, and not without some basis of truth, that the prairie dog will seal off and try to entomb a rattlesnake that is visiting a dog town.

At the first sign of a stranger, a prairie dog utters a shrill whistle of warning. All its fellows stop whatever they are doing and look about to see what the trouble is. If there seems to be any danger, they plunge to the safety of their underground home. Each individual has its own particular den, and makes a scramble for it.

No matter how grave the danger, none must enter the wrong den; if one is confused and tries to take refuge in a neighbour's retreat, the proprietor drives it away in self-righteous fury.

Eating, Sleeping, and Mating. Like the marmot, the prairie dog feeds on green vegetation. If this gets scarce, it digs down to the roots and devours them. When there is a plague of locusts or grasshoppers, the prairie dog will join forces with insect-eaters to eliminate the destroyers.

The prairie dog is not strictly a hibernating animal. At high altitudes and on the colder parts of its range, it will sleep through the winter, but in southern localities it is active the year round.

The young—they average four or six in a litter—come early in May, in an underground nest. Four weeks later they are getting their first glimpse of the upper world and seeing how plants taste in comparison to mother's milk.

Two Kinds of Prairie Dogs. There are two main kinds of prairie dogs. The Black-tailed Prairie Dog is about a foot long without its three-inch bobtail; it weighs three pounds or so. Its general colour is buff or cinnamon. Except for its smaller size and the white tip it has on its tail, the White-tailed Prairie Dog looks much like its black-tailed relative.

The prairie dog's range is comparatively small, extending over the Great Plains and the Rocky Mountain region of the United States; they are also found in southern Canada and northern Mexico. Their life span is about seven or eight years.

CHIPMUNKS—FRIENDLY CREATURES
OF THE NORTHLAND

The inquisitive, pert little chipmunks, with their bright colours and friendly disposition, add a warm, cheerful note to the countryside. They are creatures of sunlit woods and open pastures. The shrill, lively call of one will bring responses from another and another until the woods ring with their merry chatter.

Chipmunks are bold and confident when there is a safe retreat at hand. Some even have courage enough to accept a proffered morsel of food from the hand of a total stranger. Often in the lonely forests of the North-west, far from human habitation, when the author had paused to rest on a fallen tree, a chipmunk would climb up alongside in a friendly gesture that always brought a reassuring feeling of companionship.

Chipmunks do not live in the trees, neither do they choose to live on the ground; they favour stone walls, rocks, and fallen timber, especially naked branches bleached by the hot summer sun. Like most other ground squirrels, we find them only in the Northern Hemisphere; Asia and North America are the home of the chipmunk tribe.

The American chipmunks are separated into two distinct groups that have divided the continent between them. There is no overlapping of territory except around Lake Superior, in Canada.

The Eastern Chipmunk, or Hacker, *Tamais,* is a small ground-dwelling squirrel, nine or ten inches long; almost half of this is bushy tail. We can readily recognize this fellow by the five heavy black lines running down the back.

The chipmunk's home is underground. To build its den, it first sinks a sloping shaft down in the earth to a depth of about three feet. At the end of this tunnel, it makes a number of chambers, some for sleeping in and some for food storage. It does not leave the excavated earth in a tell-tale heap, but spreads it out in the bushes or tall grass. At times it will plug up the entrance to keep undesirable visitors away.

——HOME LIFE OF THE EASTERN CHIPMUNK. There is no doubt that the chipmunk likes company. Still, its social gatherings include no more than family groups—several individuals occupy the same den in winter and share a common store of food.

The chief foods sought by the chipmunk are seeds, grains, nuts, and berries. All summer long, and especially in the autumn, these busy little squirrels are out gathering food and transporting it to their storehouses underground. They carry it in their cheek pouches. An individual can transport a tablespoonful of seeds or as many as seventeen hazelnuts at a time.

——LIGHT SLEEPERS. The chipmunk's storerooms often contain half a bushel of nuts, dried fruits, and seeds. This extensive storing of food clearly shows us that the chipmunks do not pass through a long period of complete hibernation during the winter; real hibernators fatten up in advance, and live off the fat on their bodies while they are asleep.

CHIPMUNKS ARE GROUND SQUIRRELS

The chipmunk is a ground-dwelling squirrel, and makes its home below the surface. The little fellow shown above in the act of consuming a tasty morsel is the eastern chipmunk. Note the typical dark stripes on the animal's back.

During part of the winter, however, the chipmunks indulge in a short, uninterrupted torpid sleep. At other times they are awake, but stay below ground. They are out on bright sunny days very early in the spring in the middle United States.

——MATING TIME. Now begins the mating season, and the male

chipmunk sets out to pay his respects to a prospective female. Court-ship is no haphazard affair. The female must be cautiously wooed—an over-eager suitor may be tossed unceremoniously aside, to nurse the wounds inflicted by an unimpressed female.

By March most of the females have mated, and five weeks later about six young are born. From the very beginning the stripes are visible under the babies' skin. They can recognize sounds when three weeks old, and open their eyes at the end of the first month. At the ripe old age of three months, the young are well developed and able to look after themselves.

——THE CHIPMUNK CLOSE UP. If you look at an eastern chipmunk closely, you will see that the central stripe on its back is bordered on each side by a brownish line, while the two outermost stripes are separated by white. The head, with two white stripes on each cheek, is rather pointed for a squirrel. The ears are low and rounded, and the tail bushy and flattened. The warm rusty-red shades on the hips add to the colourful appearance of this little sun-worshipper.

The eastern chipmunk is spread over the greater part of eastern Canada, and the eastern United States except Florida. It is found west to the Great Plains, but here the range stops abruptly.

Other Chipmunks. The Western Chipmunk, *Eutamias*, is more slender than the eastern chipmunk, and has a relatively longer tail. The general impression is that it has many more stripes, but its normal pattern consists of five blackish and four whitish stripes, all approxi-mately equal in width, and all but the outer pair extending from the shoulders to the rump; the middle line reaches the head.

This creature occupies all of North America, west of the plains regions. Its range extends from the Yukon south into central Mexico and overlaps the range of the eastern chipmunk in Ontario and Wisconsin.

——A SIBERIAN RELATIVE. Slightly larger than the western chip-munk is its Siberian cousin, the Asiatic Chipmunk, *Eutamias sibiricus*. Fully grown, it is about ten or eleven inches long; half of this is tail.

Uniformly reddish or greyish, this animal has on its back five broad black lines separated by four light-coloured stripes. Its pelt is used by the fur trade under the name of Borunduki.

GROUND SQUIRRELS, SPERMOPHILES, AND SUSLIKS

We have already had a look at a number of ground squirrels known by other names. Now we come to those that are popularly called ground squirrels. They are robust creatures, and have a rounded head, short ears, and short legs. Their bushy tails do not match the magnificence of those of their tree-dwelling cousins', but are medium to short in length.

AN EATER OF SEEDS AND GRAIN

The golden chipmunk, a native of the American West, is one of the most attractive of the ground squirrels in its striped, rusty chestnut mantle. This active little rodent quickly seeks safety in an underground burrow when it detects the presence of its dreaded enemies, the hawk, fox, badger, weasel, and coyote.

In a characteristic pose, ground squirrels sit up on their hind feet when they want to look around. For this reason, they are often called picket pins. They will remain motionless in this position for quite a while, but when they suspect that the intentions of an intruder are harmful, they utter a shrill whistle and dive into their holes.

Most ground squirrels are social animals, and live in densely populated squirrel towns under the ground. They feed largely on green vegetation in the spring and early summer. Later in the year they devote their attention to seeds. They balance this vegetarian diet with grasshoppers, cicadas, and many other insects.

The ground squirrels hibernate during a great part of the year. They often enter their winter dens as early as July and August and rarely come out before winter is over, late in January or early February. Their families, born about thirty days after mating time, are usually large; seven to ten are not unusual in a litter, and occasionally we find twelve or thirteen babies. There is not time to raise more than one litter a year, which may be one of the reasons for the large families.

The different species vary greatly in their size and colour pattern. Many of them follow a uniform scheme of yellows, greys or browns dotted with white, but some are outstanding in their colour pattern of dots and lines. They range from the size of a chipmunk to that of a grey squirrel.

We find the ground squirrels in many different parts of the world. In North America these animals occupy a large portion of the continent from the Arctic coast to Mexico; however, they are conspicuous by their absence in both the eastern parts of Canada and the eastern United States. In the Old World, we meet ground squirrels in southeastern Europe, central Asia eastward into Siberia, as well as in the warmer parts of Africa. Many are known as Spermophiles (genus Citellus—"little quick one"—and its relatives).

The Thirteen-striped Ground Squirrel or Spermophile, *Citellus tridecemlineatus*, is an ornate little squirrel that dwells on the plains and prairies of the Middle West. Its remarkable coat is decorated with thirteen to fifteen alternating stripes and lines of "stars". Because of this décor, it is often called the "federation squirrel"; the name "striped gopher", sometimes applied to it, is a misnomer.

The striped ground squirrel is up and about when the sun rises, and remains out on the midwestern prairies during the heat of a midsummer day. It has departed from a strict vegetarian diet—half of its daily rations consist of grasshoppers, insects, and field mice, and it will also devour birds' eggs and fledgelings.

While common in some localities, this creature is not sociable, and lives a fairly lonely life. Its voice is a birdlike trill, or trembling whistle —a long drawn-out "chur-r-r-r" in a high key.

Other Ground Squirrels. In Canada's northland the Columbia Ground Squirrel, *Citellus columbianus*, ranges north on to the Arctic tundra and in the mountains of the North-west up to altitudes of eight thousand feet. It is an inquisitive squirrel, always showing up when least expected.

Its relative, the Antelope Squirrel, reminds us of the antelope as its white tail flashes against the dun-coloured body. It is a chunky little squirrel with white stripes on its sides. A lover of warm sunshine, it is one of the few ground squirrels that do not hibernate.

CREATURE OF THE BARREN WASTES

The Asiatic ground squirrel is at home in the sandy country and on the steppes of Asia. In such barren surroundings, it leads a gay, carefree life, but it always keeps an eye open for the approach of a foe. This rodent feeds on seeds, vegetable matter, and some insects. Its retreat is a burrow in the earth.

The Golden-mantled Ground Squirrel, with its brightly coloured coat of both dark and light stripes, is the most talkative of its kind. It has quite a large vocabulary of chirps, buzzes, grunts, and sometimes fairly screams when in a rage during a fight. It also makes a low ticking sound accompanied by flicks of its tail. This handsome fellow favours open woods on the mountain slopes of western North America, from six thousand feet above sea level up to thirteen thousand feet.

The California Ground Squirrel and the Rock Squirrel, of the

Rocky Mountain region, from Utah to Mexico, are the largest of the ground squirrels. Though typical ground-dwellers, they often climb oak trees in the autumn to get the acorns, and other nut-bearing trees in search of food.

———THE SUSLIK. The European Ground Squirrel, *Citellus citellus*, is generally known as the Suslik, or Souslik. We find this yellowish-brown animal from Silesia and Bohemia east across central Asia. It loves the wide-open spaces of the earth, and the drier the climate the happier it is. A great digger, it dwells in deep burrows; generally it prefers sandy wastes for its home, but all the steppe country of middle Asia is friendly to it. (It is, however, not so common in America as another species, Eversmann's Ground Squirrel.)

Susliks must have many enemies, for they are never off guard. They take every precaution for their own safety. Still, at the same time, these jolly little desert dwellers are independent and impertinent. They sit up and whistle at you, cocksure of their safety on a sand dune eighty yards away, and they never let you get any closer. They move lizard-like with well-spread legs and make a wide track over the soft sand.

Many susliks do not hibernate. For their rest they choose the summer-time, when the heat is intense. They retire to the cool earth and stay below, taking a long siesta, sometimes until the autumn.

Africa's ground squirrels, found in most of the warmer parts of the continent, are much like some of the American ground squirrels.

FLYING SQUIRRELS—THEY DO NOT FLY

Despite their name, the flying squirrels of the Northern Hemisphere are not really fliers, but gliders. Their "flying" equipment consists of thin, loose furry membranes extending on each side of the body between the fore and hind limbs.

As the animal, perched on some lofty bough, launches itself into the air, it spreads its legs, drawing the membranes taut. This wide expanse gives the squirrel enough support to permit it to glide in a downward course for a considerable distance. Before landing, the squirrel checks its speed by manipulating its tail, and comes to rest head up on the trunk of a tree.

The flying squirrel cannot sustain its flight for any long period of time: it lacks propelling organs like the wings of a bat or bird. Still, it can glide through the air up to a distance of eighty yards or more. Its driving power is really the pull of gravity, aided by the muscular effort it makes when it leaps from a high position. However, this animal can control its direction and speed.

GLIDING THROUGH THE NIGHT

Flying squirrels are active only during the night, and their large eyes are modified for seeing in dim light. They leap from tree to tree in the dark forest as the true squirrels do in the daytime. Without their sharp vision and their ability to control their flight, they could hardly do this, since they cannot see their landing point clearly until they are quite close to it.

HOME LIFE IN THE TREE DEN

During the hours of daylight, the flying squirrel rests and naps. Its bedroom may be the hollow limb of a tree twenty or thirty feet above the ground or an outside nest, made of shredded bark. If the squirrel

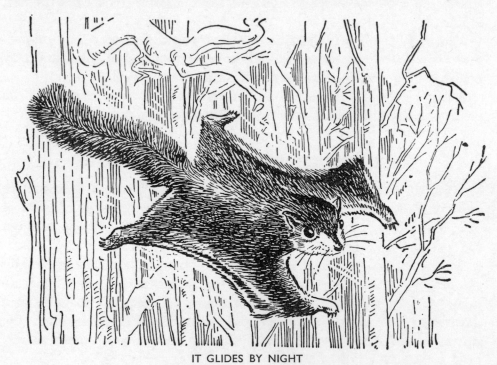

IT GLIDES BY NIGHT

The flying squirrel, as you may observe, has no true wings, and is not a flier in any sense of the word. But it can travel for many yards by gliding, with the assistance of the furry membrane it has on each side of its body.

The hoary marmot lives in the high mountains of north-western America and north-eastern Siberia. Constantly on the watch with far-reaching eyesight, its piercing, high-pitched whistle at the approach of a stranger can be heard a mile away. *See page 271*

[3-7A]

The yellow-bellied marmot or rock chuck is the "groundhog" of the western United States. Larger and more colourful than its eastern cousin, the woodchuck, it otherwise shares all the family characteristics. *See page 271*

[3-8]

Accustomed to a life of complete ease and comfort in a well-designed under-ground burrow, this flood-trapped woodchuck is really "out on a limb".

See page 268

[3-8A]

The friendly, inquisitive little chipmunk can carry a tablespoonful of seeds in its cheek pouches at one time. A tiny ground squirrel, mostly tail, it may store as much as half a bushel of nuts, dried fruits and seeds for winter use.

See page 277

[3-9]

The prairie dog, like the buffalo, is a symbol of the "vanishing" American West. Although extremely co-operative in community ventures, nobody is ever welcome in his neighbour's home, and when a prairie dog dives down the 12-foot almost vertical entrance shaft into a burrow, it had better be his own!

See page 273

[3-10]

Some ground squirrels are *known* as ground squirrels. The 13-striped ground squirrel is also called "federation squirrel" because of its stars-and-stripes markings.   *See page 279*

[3-10A]

Most talkative of the family, the golden mantled ground squirrel has the largest vocabulary. Equipped with a variety of chirps, buzzes and grunts, it also makes a low ticking noise and, angered, fairly screams with rage. *See page 280*

The California squirrel is one of the largest of the group. Although a confirmed ground dweller, it will climb nut-bearing trees in the autumn in search of food.   *See page 280*

[3-10B]

A parka stands in the typical ground squirrel attentive pose which gives them their familiar name "picket pins".   *See page 278*

[3-10C]

is small enough, a hole abandoned by a woodpecker will suffice. When the squirrel moves in, it cleans out the old nest and installs a soft bed of finely shredded bark and lichens. Now the animal has a home for many years to come.

In the flying squirrel's tree den—or in the leafy nest in the treetops —the young, numbering from one to six, are born about April, forty days after mating time. They are naked and pink at first, with their eyes and ears sealed tight. Their flying membranes are already well developed, but at this stage are fine, transparent webs of skin.

The babies open their eyes at the twenty-sixth or twenty-eighth day, and are nursed for about five weeks in all. The mother will bravely protect them from almost any danger, gliding off with them to another tree if necessary. When three months old, they have changed their baby coats for the thick fur of the adult, and by now have learned to climb and glide.

Family ties are not easily broken. The young of the year may continue to live with their mother until the following spring. Some are ready to breed at the end of the first year, but others are two years old before they raise families of their own. They have a life expectancy of about six years.

HOW THEY GET THEIR FOOD

Flying squirrels feed on much the same kind of food as the typical tree squirrels. Nuts, seeds, berries, and insects constitute the bulk of their diet. In the winter and early spring they dine off the buds and shoots of trees. Since these creatures do not hibernate, they collect a good supply of imperishable provender and store it in "warehouses" for winter use.

Though really not carnivorous, flying squirrels will never lose an opportunity to feast on meat or fat. They will on occasion kill and eat sleeping birds, and also eat birds' eggs. They must have water to drink, especially in hot weather. The author has frequently found flying squirrels drowned in water tanks, especially in the woods.

Trappers in northern forests often find these rodents troublesome. The animals fly into the traps after the bait, thus interfering with the capture of valuable fur bearers. Otherwise the feeding habits of the flying squirrels are not injurious to man and may be of some use in insect control.

EAL / 3—D

WHERE WE MEET THEM

Flying squirrels are spread far and wide over the Northern Hemisphere. We encounter them throughout the forested regions of Europe, and in Asia from eastern Siberia south to the Malay region. In North America they range from the limit of tree growth in the north, south to Honduras in Central America. All in all, there are thirteen genera (they make up the subfamily Petauristinae).

There are no flying squirrels in South America and none in Africa or Australia; the so-called "scaly-tailed flying squirrel" of Africa is not a squirrel at all.

Giants and Pygmies. These gliders reach their greatest development in the warmer parts of southern Asia, the home of the Giant Flying Squirrel, *Petaurista*. There are many variations of this creature, coloured from fox red to white or black; it may be as much as three feet in total length. At the other extreme is Borneo's Pygmy Flying Squirrel, a little over seven inches long (some four inches are the tail).

North America's Flying Squirrels. The North American Flying Squirrel, *Glaucomys*, is spread over the continent as far south as Honduras. There are two species: the Greater or Northern Flying Squirrel (it is a foot long, over-all) frequenting the wooded parts of Alaska and Canada, and south in the eastern United States to Massachusetts, and in the mountains of the west to California; and the Lesser or Southern Flying Squirrel (nine inches long), which is found in the eastern northern states west to the Great Plains and south into Central America. Both have long, soft, fine fur, varying in colour from light to dark buff. The tail is flattened and feathery, and the eyes are dark and large.

POCKET GOPHERS—A LIFE IN TOTAL DARKNESS

The pocket gopher spends almost its entire life underground in total darkness. Not even a streak of light is permitted to penetrate its maze of subterranean passageways. It is a spectacular digger, like the mole —a single gopher can excavate a tunnel two or three hundred feet long in one night. At regular intervals, as it digs, it makes a temporary surface opening and forces the loosened excavated earth out through it, but promptly and securely plugs up the hole afterwards, for safety's sake.

This mining machine of flesh and blood looks as though it had been designed for its work. Short legged and thickset, the pocket gopher has no appreciable neck. Its ears are barely noticeable, its eyes minute and almost sightless. Its forefeet, armed with strong, curved claws, are first-rate digging tools, but where the ground is excessively hard the animal brings its strong, chisel like front teeth into action.

The pocket gopher is one of the few animals that can run backwards as fast and as easily as it can move forward. Here its tail serves it in good stead. Fleshy and of moderate length, the tail is endowed with tactile organs, enabling the animal to feel its way around underground when it moves in reverse.

The pocket gopher actually has pockets, from which it gets its name. The pockets are large cheek pouches that open to the outside of its face and reach back to its shoulders. They are lined with fur, and the gopher uses them for one purpose only, to carry food—not dirt as has often been supposed. (The word "gopher", by the way, comes from the French *gaufre*, meaning "waffle" or "honeycomb", an allusion to the maze of tunnels the animal makes.)

It would be a mistake to think that the gopher never ventures above ground; quite frequently one will come out to get some green vegetation, but during the time it spends on the surface it is nervous and fidgety, as if fearful of being snatched up by some prowling beast of prey.

Its food includes roots and tubers, and stems of grasses that can be secured below the surface of the ground, or drawn into the tunnels from below.

A SPACIOUS APARTMENT UNDERGROUND

Gophers are great hoarders, and fill their storehouses with much more food than they can possibly consume. Hoarding is a necessity, as they do not hibernate in the colder parts of their range, and much of the ground where they secure their food is frozen solid during winter.

Each gopher has up to eight or nine storage rooms; all may be kept packed with roots and tubers. When the ground is covered with snow, the gopher may also use snow tunnels and feed on surface vegetation.

The gopher's nest is located close to the storage rooms. It is a round ball of finely shredded leaves and grass, about nine or ten inches through, and may be at various depths, depending on the temperature and moisture in the ground. In wet lowlands a gopher may even raise a mound of earth six feet in diameter and two feet high in which to have a comfortable dry nest.

Gophers, like many other underground dwellers, make toilets for their own use, and periodically close them off and dig new ones.

AN ANIMATED MINING MACHINE

The pocket gopher, with its long, sturdy claws, is a tunneller by nature, and spends much of its time hollowing out underground passageways that will bring it close to vegetable food. It may do great damage to crops and the roots of trees. Pictured above is the western pocket gopher of North America.

HATE AND LOVE AMONG THE GOPHERS

Gophers prefer their own individual company. There is never more than one gopher in a particular chain of runways. If two accidentally meet, they fight to kill. The only time in the year that one will tolerate another is in the spring; then, just the male leaves his den to court the female, who stays in her own, awaiting his coming. About four weeks later the young are born—from one to nine in a litter. The male has long since returned to his own labyrinth of subterranean passageways.

Only the female cares for the baby gophers. At birth they are naked, and weigh about one fifth of an ounce. Their eyes and ears are sealed shut until their fifth week. However, these little creatures develop rapidly and are soon ready to eat solid food. After two months the family breaks up, the young gophers leaving the shelter of the mother's home to build their own nests.

The life of the pocket gopher, we see, is much like that of the mole, with one great difference: the gopher feeds on vegetable matter, and the mole on small animal life such as insects and worms. In the past, the gopher's digging, like the mole's, has done much to further the cultivation and preparation of the rich, fertile plains of western North America, that are today feeding the world. However, this rodent's activities under the ground are not entirely beneficial to agriculture, as we shall soon see.

WHERE THEY DWELL

Pocket gophers are strictly North and Central American animals. They range from the plains of Saskatchewan in Canada, southward to Panama, being most abundant in the western United States and Mexico.

We do not find them in the region to the east of the Mississippi Valley except in the Gulf States, where they reach the Atlantic Coast in Florida.

DIFFERENT KINDS OF "EARTH MICE"

Though very much alike in general, there are many different kinds of pocket gophers. (They make up the family Geomyidae, or "earth mice".) In size these creatures range from six to twelve inches in head-and-body length. All have fairly short tails and legs.

Almost every mountain ridge marks the boundary of a particular kind of gopher's domain. Since they spend their lives in the darkness of their tunnels, they have not specialized in fancy colours. Although there are a number of distinct kinds and an extremely large variety of geographical forms (here we shall look at only a few) the fur of most is dull brown or soil-coloured.

North American Pocket Gophers. The common pocket gopher of the Western States is the Western Pocket Gopher, *Thomomys*. Although it is only about five inches long, it is a source of constant annoyance to farmers. Not only are the mounds raised by it a menace to the reaping machines cutting the alfalfa, but it destroys the crops by eating their roots. Its endless gnawing of bulbs, tubers and the roots of fruit trees and other economically important plants causes vast destruction.

In the middle states, east of the Rockies, from the Dakotas to the Mexican boundary and in the Gulf states, this animal is replaced by the Eastern Pocket Gopher, *Geomys*, a somewhat similar creature that differs, however, in having a deep groove down the front of each upper incisor.

Pocket Gophers of Other Lands. With the exception of the Chestnut faced Pocket Gopher, *Cratogeomys*, found on the plains of south-western Colorado and Oklahoma, all the larger gophers occur in Mexico and Central America. The Giant Costa Rican Gopher, *Macrogeomys heterodus*, is one of the largest—it has a length of twelve inches without its short tail. As can readily be imagined, this big fellow is very destructive to sugar cane, banana plantations and sweet potato crops.

Cherrie's Pocket Gopher, a smaller animal, is blue black in colour and is one of the few kinds of gophers that have any distinctive colour markings. One species has a characteristic white spot on the crown of the head while another has a distinctive white girdle about the hips. These decorative colour patterns are probably an accidental development and seemingly have no value to an animal that lives in total darkness. However, since the markings in this case contribute little to the destruction of the species, they can be safely inherited by succeeding generations.

POCKET MICE AND KANGAROO RATS— NEITHER MICE NOR RATS

We generally find these little creatures in dry regions, often where there is no water whatever. Of course, no animals can live for an indefinite length of time without water in some form, but these, especially the little pocket mice, are able to extract whatever amount they need from their food. Even when the diet is limited to dry grain, they never drink.

Like the pocket gophers, the pocket mice, spiny pocket mice, and kangaroo rats are natives of North and Central America. Like the pocket gophers, too, all have fur lined cheek pouches. Still, they are not squirrels or gophers, and, although they usually have a long tail, they are not mice or rats. Their hind limbs are longer than their front ones. Beyond these common traits, they are very different from each other in appearance, although they are close relatives. (Appropriately enough, their family name—Heteromyidae—means "different mice".)

POCKET MICE—NO HEAVIER THAN AN OUNCE

The Little Pocket Mouse, *Perognathus*, is a small, dainty underground dweller with long hind limbs for jumping. Its many species include the smallest rodent on the North American continent, the Pacific Pocket Mouse, which, when fully grown, weighs only one-third of an ounce; the largest of the group, the big California Pocket Mouse, will weigh an ounce. They are found only in Western North America and do not live east of the Mississippi River. The northern limit of their homeland is Ashcraft, British Columbia; the southern is Thalpam, in the valley of Mexico.

——LITTLE DWELLER IN THE DESERT. The life of the pocket mouse is spent for the most part in dry places, where there is often no water for many months of the year. The sun in a cloudless sky, day after day, burns up all the moisture in the ground, leaving it hot and parched. In these torrid surroundings the tiny pocket mice are born and live until their last, long sleep.

As the sun goes down, these little denizens of the desert open their doors and set out on their quest for food. Standing up on their stilt-like hind legs, they pluck seeds from the grasses and plants with their tiny white hands.

Each hand independently stuffs seeds from the grasses and plants into the fur-lined cheek pouches, and moves so fast that the motion becomes a blur. The cheek pouches swell to seemingly bursting capacity. (Each pouch actually holds from one-eighth to one-half of a teaspoonful of plunder, according to the size of the species.)

Their pockets filled, in the early morning the pocket mice return to their burrows and unload their spoils with a sweeping motion of their hands.

Then the pocket mice firmly "close the door" with soil behind them.

This habit of going abroad by night is particularly advantageous in a hot climate, where there is no water. In its underground burrow the little pocket mouse is protected from the heat of the sun during the day; after sunset the desert cools rapidly.

The gentle and inoffensive pocket mice live alone except when breeding. Each mouse has its own individual little burrow. The burrow may be a simple straight tunnel with a grass-lined nest chamber at the end, or it may be a network of runways with numerous store-rooms, sometimes as long as seven feet. Normally the outside door is closed when the pocket mouse is at home, but should some predator break down the door and enter, the resourceful little mouse will put roadblocks in the way.

——POCKET MICE OLD AND YOUNG. Mating is not confined to any particular season over the entire pocket-mouse range. A female usually bears two families a year. Each comes between three and four weeks after mating; two to eight tiny babies make up the litter. A life of not more than a few months lies before them—there are too many hungry mouths waiting to devour the average pocket mouse. Its worst enemies are foxes, skunks, weasels, badgers, coyotes, snakes and owls.

In captivity, pocket mice do much better. Some have lived four or five years; one even tottered past its seventh birthday, but this was a very old mouse indeed when it died: its teeth were worn down almost to its gums.

——POCKET MICE SOFT AND SPINY. We have said there are a large number of different species of pocket mice. They fall into two well-defined groups.

Those we place in the first group possess fur that is fine and soft, while those in the second have an almost spiny coat. The general colour is in varying shades of buff, with a greater or lesser admixture of black.

These creatures are all small to tiny in size. An animal of average size is about five inches long, and often the tail is almost half of this.

SPINY POCKET MICE—THEY HATE COLD WEATHER

Protected Against Cactus and Insect Bites. About the size of a large mouse or small rat, the spiny pocket mouse has a long, well-haired tail, and fur-lined cheek pouches like the pocket gopher and the pocket mouse pure and simple. The coat that gives it its name is made up of dark-brown hair mixed with stiff, flattened spines and helps us to tell it from its immediate relatives.

Why the spines? They are no defence against the mortal enemies of the pocket mice: snakes, foxes, cats, weasels and the like. Still, they may afford some degree of protection against cactus thorns or insect bites.

Night-time Foragers. Tropical and subtropical America, from southern Texas to Ecuador, is the home of these creatures. They dwell in warm, arid places—often in the open desert—but are also found in humid forests. Burrowers, they keep house in a series of underground tunnels, and make sure that the door to the outer world is always securely closed. They rarely open it before nightfall, when they go foraging for nuts, seeds, and grass. This quest takes them into cultivated fields sometimes, to the detriment of farmers.

A Habit Out of the Distant Past? While the spiny pocket mice always avoid bright warm sunlight, they abhor cold weather. This looks like a contradiction, but so do many mammal habits. Perhaps the reason is to be found in the far past.

Along with the pocket mice and pocket gophers, the spiny pocket mice seem to have originated in Central America. Possibly all three achieved their development when this part of the world was separated by geographical or climatic conditions from the north and south, and they were not subjected to the extremes of temperature they have to put up with today.

Though very different in appearance, the three groups have many strange features and habits in common, especially their hermit-like life, the urge to hoard food where it does not seem to be an absolute necessity, and cheek pouches in which to carry it to their storage rooms.

Spiny Pocket Mouse Babies. Mother spiny pocket mouse may bear her babies, up to five in number, at almost any season of the year. They are well furred when they come into the world, but their flat spines are soft. Two months later the now half-grown youngsters shed their baby fur and get a new, shining coat of stiff, sharp bristles, the trade mark of their breed.

There are two main kinds of spiny pocket mice. The Lesser Spiny Pocket Mouse, *Liomys*, the more northerly type, is mouse-grey above, white below and on its limbs. It is about five inches long, with a tail of equal length. The Greater Spiny Pocket Mouse, *Heteromys*, is a few inches longer, and more extensively black.

KANGAROO RATS—FRIENDLY JUMPERS
OF THE DESERT

The Kangaroo Rat, *Dipodomys*, looks like a pygmy kangaroo. One of the handsomest of the smaller rodents, it resembles the true rat only in its size. (It is about a foot long, but over seven inches of this is the tail.) In its large, oval head there are big, round, dark eyes; atop it, rather small ears.

Like a kangaroo, this quaint-looking creature sits up on its great hind legs and hops around in a series of continuous six-foot to eight-foot leaps. It uses its long tail, which is tipped with a large, feather-like brush, to maintain its balance while it is in the air.

IT NEVER TOUCHES WATER

The tiny kangaroo rat, with its powerful hind limbs, can cover more than six feet in a single leap. A creature of the American deserts and dry plains, it gets all the liquid it needs out of its food—even tame kangaroo rats are indifferent to water. This animal has large eyes, which correctly suggest that it is active by night; the kangaroo rat passes the daylight hours underground.

The kangaroo rat lives in the warm, dry parts of western North America, from Oregon and Colorado in the United States south into Mexico and as far as Veracruz. In particular it favours sandy plains thickly dotted with bushes and cacti. Here it dwells not far from others of its kind, lying up during the day in an underground burrow it has dug. Like the pocket mouse, it may keep the entrance to the passageway securely closed with dirt, except when it goes above ground in the dark, in search of seeds.

Picking the seeds from various plants, the kangaroo rat loads them into its pockets or cheek pouches with its forefeet. It fills the pockets with the hard grains so rapidly that there is a continuous rattling sound. When it has returned to its den, it ejects the loot equally fast, aiding itself with a forward squeezing motion of its forefeet. It is not unusual for one of these rats to accumulate fifty quarts of seeds in its underground store-rooms.

——How It Gets Its Water. This desert creature never drinks a drop of liquid from the day it leaves its mother's lap until it dies. It may never have a chance to drink and doesn't want to. For water, it eats small juicy tubers that grow abundantly on the desert and can be found an inch or two below the surface of the ground.

——Fighting to the Death. Except during the breeding season, kangaroo rats live alone. Put two of them together and they will fight to kill. Apparently they do not use their teeth in battle but leap and spar, striking each other with all the force of their clawed hind feet. There is no quarter expected and none given. They fight silently until one is beaten to death.

——The Babies Come. Most kangaroo rats mate in March or April. The babies, from two to five in a litter, are born with their legs and tail quite short. Like other mothers, theirs is attentive and loving. If danger threatens—the burrow may be flooded or a badger may call—she will carry off her pink little nurslings in her arms.

About fifteen days after birth the young open their eyes, and a week later are weaned. Their life span is two years or so.

——Making Friends with Kangaroo Rats. Though these galloping ghosts of the desert, as Morley Cooper, the naturalist, calls them, are timid and shy, one can gain their confidence with patience.

Mr. Cooper's first acquaintance with the miniature kangaroos was nothing more than a strange flash of sand-coloured animation he saw from his trailer parked far out on the Colorado desert. In time he had them not only eating out of his hand but responding to his call, when they would climb on to his knee for food. They loved to be stroked, but resented being held or restricted in any way; they bit viciously when he tried to seize them.

If you wish to "tame" some kangaroo rats, says Mr. Cooper, take your time about it. Begin by leaving bits of dried bread or nuts near the entrance to their burrows in the evening.

After about a week of this, wait around until the animals come out. They will at first be half-scared out of their wits, but in a few days will accept food from your hand. From then on it will not be difficult to persuade them to hop on your lap and to come out when you call them by name.

——A PRETTY "RAT". There are some nine distinct groups of kangaroo rats. The giant of the breed, the Banner-tailed Kangaroo Rat, has a length of fourteen inches, tail and all, and will weigh six and one-half ounces. The smallest, the Dwarf Kangaroo Rat, is only six or seven inches long.

These animals are beautifully coloured; the fur on the back is a soft shade of tan or grey, while the under-parts are snowy white. There is a large dash of white behind each ear, and a clear white band cuts across the back below the hips right to the tail. This colour pattern is pretty much the same throughout the eighty-two forms of kangaroo rats that have been named.

BEAVERS—NATURE'S FLOOD-CONTROL EXPERTS

The beaver, famed for its skill as a builder of dams, is also valued for the handsome, dark-brown coat of thick fur that covers it. The creature is not at all well known in the Old World, where it almost disappeared centuries ago. In the New World it continues to prosper with man's protection.

This animal is a rodent, though it is hard to think of it in that way. What is more, it is the largest member of its order that we meet in the Northern Hemisphere; in fact, the only rodent exceeding it in size is the capybara of South America.

A full-grown beaver weighs a good thirty to fifty pounds. If exceptionally large, it may come closer to one hundred. It continues to grow through life. From the tip of its nose to the end of its broad tail, this great animal measures some three or four feet. (The tail makes up about one-third of the length.)

The Beaver Loves Bark. Trees mean life to the beavers. Their favourite food is the bark of the poplar or quaking aspen, but they will seek their fare on most hardwood trees; some vegetation also finds its place in their diet. Primarily, however, they feed on the bark peeled from the top branches. To get at these, the animals have to chop the tree down.

With its powerful yellow chisel-teeth, a beaver can fell in fifteen minutes a tree four inches thick; in some instances a beaver has felled trees over five feet in diameter and over one hundred feet tall.

TALENTED WOODSMEN

The cutting is generally done by a pair of adults, helped by their grown-up children. They usually work in turns, while one keeps watch. When the tree begins to crack, they prudently desist for a while; if the tree does not come down, they continue until they see it start to fall. At that moment, all plunge into a nearby pond and seemingly wait to observe whether the noise has attracted unwelcome attention.

Occasionally a tree falls the wrong way and is prevented from coming to the ground by the branches of other trees; alas, the beavers' good labour is wasted. In rare instances they have been killed by falling timber.

Can Beavers Climb? If you were to ask the average wild-life expert: "Can beavers climb trees?" the answer would bring forth a resounding "No!"

Recently, however, there came from Nova Scotia an eye-witness account of a beaver that was seen cutting the bark of a birch tree twenty feet from the ground! The creature had not scrambled up a leaning trunk; it was actually at work on a tall straight tree. Having satisfied its hunger, it came down with a rush, leaped into a nearby pond, and spanked the water with its tail in typical beaver fashion.

The author does not mean to lead you to believe that beavers habitually climb trees—they do not—but rather that the behaviour of wild animals is unpredictable.

A SPEEDY SWIMMER

This fascinating creature's talents as a woodchopper, great though they may be, are hardly second to its skill as a swimmer. The beaver's speed under water and its lung capacity are truly remarkable: it is able to cover a quarter of a mile in fifteen minutes without coming up for air.

On the surface, the burly beaver can swim at the rate of two miles an hour, propelling itself with its webbed feet. Its flat tail acts as a rudder, and the animal certainly needs one when it is hauling a load of timber to construct a dam. By turning the tail at an angle, the beaver can set its course direct for its objective instead of being forced to travel in a more or less circular route by the unbalanced load of freight it often carries.

HOW THE BEAVER BUILDS

The beaver, you see, is no wastrel. After it has peeled off all the bark it wants, it has uses for the rest of the fallen tree. Accordingly, it proceeds to chop it up. Some parts it uses to build its house, some to form the foundation of the dams it is always constructing.

Having transported the branches to the chosen site in a stream, the animal lays them down with the thick ends side by side facing the current, and weights them with mud and rocks. It piles on layer after layer, until the desired height has been reached. Then it completes the dam with a coating of mud.

MARVELS OF BEAVER CONSTRUCTION

Building a dam is hard work, even for the industrious and powerful beaver. It has a very serious purpose in undertaking its construction jobs.

The animal, by its body and habits, is meant for a life in the water and near it. That is why it builds the dams. It wants to make certain it will have plenty of water of adequate depth close to its home, and it will get that water even if it has to block shallow streams and brooks and turn them into ponds.

How the Dams Help. One fortunate result of the beaver's work is that water conservation is helped enormously. Its dams store water during the rains for periods of drought; there are many places in the western states where farmers are dependent on the beaver for their water supply in the irrigation of their crops. Likewise, these structures help in the control of floods.

Each family of beavers creates its own particular pond by means of its dams. The water they hold back amounts to thousands of tons. It provides drink for deer, moose, and other animals, besides supplying moisture for trees and vegetation (the dams keep a trickle of water running all through the year). Beaver ponds are valuable also as forest-fire guards, and make excellent breeding places for fish.

Built to Endure. Beaver dams will stand for many years. You will find them in many different sizes. There are beaver dams three hundred feet long that contain a hundred tons of material. The record dam is believed to be one that was built in Montana—it measured 2,140 feet. The highest dam will not exceed twelve feet, with a base fifteen to twenty feet thick.

THE BEAVER AT WORK

Beavers do most of their work at night, and their labours consist largely of gnawing and felling trees, cutting them into convenient lengths, and carrying these away to build dams and houses. With its strong rodent teeth, a beaver can bring down a tree in fifteen minutes. The bark of the tree serves the animal as food.

Most do not approach these dimensions, however; the average dam is not more than four or five feet high, though it may be several hundred feet long. The larger dams are the work of many beavers, each of which adds to the pile heaped up by its predecessor.

Beaver Canals. Beaver canals are still more remarkable, not only because they may extend over one thousand feet and are often branched or forked, but because of their locks. The lock is made by raising a low dam that causes the water level to rise; over the dam the logs must be dragged.

Beaver canals are made for much the same purpose as our canals— for the transportation of freight too heavy to drag overland to the place where the animal is preparing its lodge or pond. The beaver expends considerable effort in the construction of its canals and in keeping them in repair. They are about two or three feet wide, with about eighteen inches of water throughout.

THE LODGE OF THE BEAVERS

The beaver often makes its house, or lodge, out in its pond. The dwelling is roughly conical in shape, perhaps ten to twenty feet across and four or five feet high, with walls rising abruptly from the water.

The animal uses heavy poles and thick sticks and plasters the whole structure with mud. It leaves a small chimney, or air hole, in the top for ventilation, and builds its entrance tunnel beneath the surface. Inside, there is a one-room apartment, with the floor just above water-level; on one side the animal makes itself a soft couch of shredded bark.

In the autumn, the beaver works overtime caching green branches in the mud at the bottom of the pool below the frost line. This is its winter food supply. It cuts the branches into lengths that it can easily handle, and stores them beneath the frozen surface, where it can reach them in a quick swim from its lodge. This is a wise provision. During severe winter frosts, the sap in the standing trees freezes so hard that not even the chisel-teeth of a beaver could cut them down.

Not every beaver lives in a lodge. On swift rivers, the beaver may burrow a hole in the bank, and make its chamber at the end of it. The entrance tunnel is frequently very long and is slanted downward, with its entrance right in the water.

BEAVERS ARE LOVING PARENTS

Family ties are durable among the beavers; a male and female will live together until some tragedy separates them. They mate early in the year. Two to six young, or "kittens" as they are called, are born about four months later. They are less than a foot long and weigh under

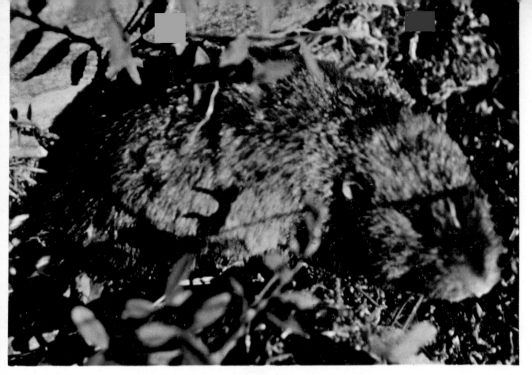

[3-11]

The pocket gopher, like the mole, is a prodigious digger and spends almost all of its life underground. It has "pockets"—fur-lined cheek pouches that open to the outside, in which it carries food.   *See page 284*

[3-11A]

The kangaroo rat also has fur-lined cheek pouches, but it is not a gopher, or a rat. It does leap like a kangaroo and covers an average of 17 times its body length in one hop, using its long brush-tipped tail to maintain balance.
See page 292

[3-12]

The broad shovel tail of the beaver is useful not only for carrying mud to plaster its ingenious building projects, but also as a rudder directing the course as it swims with a heavy load of timber.   *See page 294*

[3-12A]

Beavers usually build their homes in ponds of their own construction. The entrance is below the surface, but the floor is above water-level, and there is a small chimney or air-hole at the top for ventilation. A male and female beaver live together until some tragedy separates them.   *See page 294* a pound each. Their eyes are open from the first, and they are covered with soft fur.

The kittens mature slowly. In spite of the fact that they are out learning to swim when a month old and are weaned after six months, they remain under their parents' care for about a year. Their father and mother are good parents and spend much time training and instructing the kittens.

When the young beavers are close to two years old, breeding time comes again. Last year's family, that have lived in the shelter of the parents' home until now, take their departure just before the arrival of the new family. It may be that the mother suddenly forces them to leave, or perhaps they get the wanderlust. But go they must. Even the dutiful protector and father must seek quarters elsewhere for the time being.

Alone now, the prospective mother gathers new materials for her children's crib—finely shredded bark and other soft materials. She heaps them all on the nursery floor, a raised platform in the lodge. Then she waits for her babies to come. Thus life is handed on in the world of the beavers. Ten or twelve years is as long as these animals live in the wild; nineteen years is the record under the easier circumstances of captivity.

BEAVERS AROUND THE WORLD

The beaver is active by night, more or less, and though it is common in some localities, we rarely see it between seven-thirty in the morning and sunset. The American Beaver, *Castor canadensis*, is found in the forests of North America, from Alaska and Labrador to the Rio Grande. Close to two hundred thousand skins of this species are taken every year, half of them in Canada.

The Eurasian Beaver, *Castor fiber*, used to dwell throughout the entire forested region of Europe and east in Asia to Mongolia. It is now restricted to eastern Europe, remote parts of Scandinavia, Finland, Siberia, and Mongolia. Though some authors report it to be a burrower, on the whole it behaves much like its American cousin, building lodges and dams and cutting trees. However, a large percentage of the Old World beavers are bank-dwellers.

Made for a Life in the Water. It would not be fair to leave the beavers without taking a quick look at the remarkable equipment they possess for their life in the water. We have already noted the broad, scaly tail, and how the animal uses it in swimming. The hind feet are large and webbed for propulsion in the water; the front feet are relatively small.

Nature has even provided the beaver with a comb for its superb coat; the second toe of its hind foot is cleft, and the beaver uses this to groom itself when it emerges dripping from a stream. Its small ears, like its nose, are equipped with valves that shut these organs securely when the animal goes on an underwater trip.

Keeping its mouth open underwater poses a serious problem for any animal. How does the beaver carry branches in its open mouth below the surface? The answer is that it has loose lips, and can draw them in behind its front teeth and seal them together, permitting it to use the teeth freely and hold objects with them when it is submerged. Because of its large lungs and liver, the beaver is able to carry a considerable amount of air and oxygen-rich blood for its extended stays under the water.

"DEVIL'S CORKSCREWS" AND GIANT BEAVERS

The beaver (family Castoridae) has been with us for a long time indeed. For a good many years, farmers in Wyoming, South Dakota, and Nebraska were puzzled by hard, lengthy, spiral-shaped formations they used to encounter when they dug into their land. Scientists were unable to offer a satisfactory explanation of these strange things. The name they gave them was "daimonelix", but the formations were popularly known as "devil's corkscrews". Ultimately, their riddle was solved.

From fossils that have been found, we now know that giant beavers, seven and one-half feet from nose to tip, once lived in North America. The time was many thousands of years ago, during the later glacial periods. Some of these primitive relatives of the beaver dwelt in underground burrows, which they excavated in the form of spirals. Later the burrows were filled with vegetable débris that became fossilized— much harder than the surrounding earth—resulting in the "devil's corkscrews".

Thus another of Nature's mysteries, when explained, was not mysterious at all, but a reminder that life on this planet is infinitely varied and of great antiquity.

AFRICA'S SCALY-TAILED "SQUIRRELS"

The scaly-tailed "squirrels", at home in central and western Africa, are not squirrels at all. What is more, it is not obvious at first glance that these little creatures are scaly-tailed.

Look at a scaly-tailed squirrel closely, however, and you will see, on the underside of the tail, near the base, peculiar scaly outgrowths. The scales have sharp, protruding edges which conveniently project backwards and serve the animal as anchors or climbing irons that help support it in the trees.

The scaly-tailed squirrels spend the day sleeping in hollow trees. They frequent the heavy forest, where the timber towers some 135 feet skyward, and use holes that may be situated from ten to 120 feet above the ground. Often the natives of the Congo smoke the animals out by starting a fire at the base of the tree and then kill them and use them for food.

GLIDERS OF THE TROPICAL NIGHT

Most of the scaly-tailed squirrels are gliders. They leave their roosts soon after sunset. There is very little twilight in the tropical regions where they live, and once they are on the prowl it is hard to see them in the gloom.

In the dark, the scaly-tailed squirrel runs swiftly up tree trunks and along branches until it reaches the uppermost limbs. Here it pauses briefly before launching itself into the empty void. With a sudden spring, it sails outward and downward.

For an instant you may see the animal's almost square silhouette against the starlit sky. Then it has vanished from sight—to land on the trunk of a tree sometimes sixty or eighty feet away. Soon it repeats the performance. Caught in the glare of a flashlight, its big eyes shine with a dull yellow glow.

Gliding Equipment. Like other gliders, this one, you have observed, is a creature of the night. It has much the same sort of gliding equipment as other gliders, too.

In its short aerial voyages, the animal is supported by flight membranes—thin, furry folds of skin on its sides, stretching between its fore and hind limbs. On its elbow the scaly-tailed squirrel has a long, slender spur which it can extend outward to draw the membrane still tauter.

For added support, it has an extension of the flying membrane spread between its hind feet and the base of its tail.

AT REST AND IN FLIGHT

The scaly-tailed squirrel makes its home in the trees of the African jungle. It can run nimbly from branch to branch but its greatest talent is for gliding—a sixty-foot flight is by no means a record for one of these animals. What is even more impressive, they make their glides in the dark.

Some Well-known Scaly-tails. These African gliders live either singly or in pairs, and feed on nuts, fruits, seeds, and the like. As a group, they have no close relatives; they form a distinct family of their own (Anomaluridae, which means "exceptional tails"). Best known, and one of the largest, is the Grey Scaly-tailed Glider, *Anomalurus*—it has a head-and-body length of twelve inches, with a tail a little shorter.

Oddity of the group is the Scaly-tailed Tree "Squirrel", *Zenkerella*, which lacks the flight membranes but otherwise resembles its gliding cousins quite closely.

SPRINGHAAS—JUMPING HARES OF AFRICA

The Springhaas, *Pedetes*, of East and South Africa, got its name from the Boers. Springhaas means "jumping hare", and we often call it that in English.

This sandy-coloured creature is about a foot high sitting on its haunches. It has a lengthy, hairy tail with a thick black brush at the tip. Its large, rounded head bears prominent and widely separated ears, which tend to fall to one side. Although timid by nature, it is attracted to camps, and at night one occasionally sees its big, round eyes shining like balls of fire, flashing back a beam of light.

The springhaas has long hind limbs and feet and gets about much like the kangaroo, progressing by remarkable two-footed leaps and bounds. Searching for food, it often journeys six to twelve miles a night. In times of severe drought it may travel a distance of twenty miles in one night to parts where rain has recently fallen.

On its long jaunts it frequently follows highways and Kaffir paths; here its movements can be easily observed.

FARMER'S PEST AND BUSHMAN'S BLESSING

The natural fare of this little African consists of bulbs and roots, which it digs out of the ground with the strong, curved claws on its front feet. It is very destructive to grain crops. Systematically it uproots the young plants to get at the seed below. It will also eat the ripened grain.

Home Life of the Springhaas. The springhaas lives in burrows or warrens scattered over an area of about a hundred yards. The warrens often have four to eight openings, and may be used jointly by a pair of animals, but there are no community dens. These creatures have a curious way of sleeping—sitting up on their haunches. They never come out before dark, and generally go underground before daylight, closing the "door" behind them with plugs of earth. If disturbed, they may erect two or three such barricades.

The springhaas is not a fast breeder. A single baby in a litter is normal; twins are rare. Still, the animal seems to maintain its numbers, even in populated districts.

When common, the springhaas forms one of the main sources of food for the natives. Bushmen catch it with the aid of several reeds tied together to form a single flexible rod, fifteen or twenty feet in length. There is a large wire hook fastened to one end, and they push this down the burrow, and twist it about until eventually the animal is hooked and dragged out.

The springhaas family (Pedetidae, a name meaning "leapers") is a "problem child" for naturalists. It has no living relatives, and even fossil forms are not found outside Africa. There are no giant or dwarf springhaas, the animals forming one general tribe.

Scurriers, Jumpers, Swimmers and Burrowers—Mice, Rats and their Kin

GERMAN FOLKLORE has a legend about a talented piper who had a way with rodents. His tunes, we are told, charmed all the rats of Hamelin to such a degree that they cheerily drowned themselves in the River Weser. Well, it would take a legion of virtuosos like him to rid the world of the incredibly enormous and specialized armies of mice, rats, and their relatives that occupy it. Their realm stretches almost from Pole to Pole.

For most of us, the word "mouse" or the word "rat" conjures up an annoying picture of the common household variety of these animals. It is a false picture, however—the domestic mice and rats form only the tiniest fraction of the group of rodents to which this chapter is devoted: the "myomorphs" or "mouselike" rodents (suborder Myomorpha). Quite a number of the wild members of this group are handsome little creatures, beautifully furred, with ways and habits as fascinating as those of the tiger, the hippopotamus, the lion, and the elephant, on a small scale.

So, before we proceed any farther, you would be wise to banish from your mind all traditional ideas you may have about rodents as such, and let the behaviour of the creatures speak for itself. That there are pleasing wonders of animal life in store for you here, the author can safely guarantee.

The "mouselike" rodents are the most abundant of all. Why, just one family alone, which we shall immediately turn to, has over seventy imposing groups to it with generic names! Simply to call the roll of their species and subspecies would be a gigantic task.

We may, however, mention a few, to give you some idea of the variety we find in this family—Rice Rats, Water Rats, Harvest Mice, White-footed Mice, Wood Rats, Cotton Rats, Muskrats, Voles, Lemmings, Field Mice, Spiny Mice, Tree Rats, Vesper Rats, Grass-hopper Mice, Pygmy Mice, Little Brown Mice, Leaf-eared Mice, Gerbils, Antelope Rats—but here we had better desist, before we succumb to the notion that they, and not we, are the masters of the earth. Indeed, they almost are, for their hordes include all the mice and rats of the New World, as well as many in Europe, Asia, Africa, and Madagascar. Perhaps the most popular member of this family (Cricetidae) is a little Eurasian that has now been adopted in the United States, the Hamster, *Cricetus*, after which the family is named.

NEW WORLD RATS, MICE, VOLES, GERBILS AND THEIR OLD WORLD RELATIVES

The Rice Rat, *Oryzomys*, is a little creature of a cleanly nature, and does not enter human dwellings. It is very much at home throughout South and Central America and Mexico; we find it from Patagonia north to Texas and, on the Atlantic seaboard, as far north as New Jersey. It is the common rodent of tropical America, just as the house rat is of Europe and Asia.

The name "rice rat" was given to this small animal because it was once extremely abundant in the rice fields of the south-eastern United States, doing considerable damage to the crops when rice was extensively grown there. Actually, the rice rat is misnamed, for it does not favour rice so much as it does green grass stems. Every week it consumes almost twice its weight in food.

The rice rat is a good diver and swimmer. It prefers to live in meadows and marshy areas near water (this is true of the North American species), though some individuals are found at high altitudes, especially along watercourses. The animal spends the day in its nest of plant fibres, which it places in a shallow burrow or under masses of vegetation. In the tidewater marshes it elevates the nest in the reeds and bushes to be above high-water level.

——AN AGGRESSIVE FEMALE. In warm climates, the rice rat breeds the year round. The female does not stay at home waiting to be wooed, but goes out looking for a mate.

Courtship is short with this fickle lady—it never lasts more than a few hours. Then, unceremoniously, she turns on her mate and drives him out. Twenty-five days later, and ten hours after her family of four or five is born, Mrs. Rice Rat is out searching for a new mate.

When twelve days old, the babies are weaned and their mother drives them out into the world. She must get about her main business—she produces up to eight or ten litters a year—and she has to be prepared to care for her new family. Since the young are ready to breed when they are seven weeks old, you can judge for yourself how great are the numbers of these animals.

The rice rat is a fighter and a killer. It feels no qualms about devouring its own kind. Not only does its own belligerent nature help to keep its numbers in check; its natural enemies, the owls, snakes, and weasels, will often pounce upon it in the night, when it is active, or seek it in its nest.

——THE LONG AND SHORT OF IT. There are more than 180 different kinds of rice rat, and many vary greatly in size. On an average, they are a foot in length, or shorter, tail and all. The Pygmy Rice Rat, *Oligoryzomys*, of north-eastern South America, is no bigger than a house mouse; at the other extreme there is a so-called "Muskrat", *Megalomys*, dwelling in the Lesser Antilles, with a total length up to thirty inches. Species found in the United States are about the size of an overgrown house mouse.

Rice rats vary in colour, too. They range from pale shades of buff or grey to rich tawny or russet, more or less mixed with black. Their fur is often rather coarse and fairly long. They have a scantily haired tail, usually about three-quarters the length of the head and body.

Other Rats and Mice of Central and South America. The tropical regions of America support rats and mice in great numbers, but we must content ourselves with mentioning only one, the Vesper Rat, *Nyctomys* ("night mouse"). This, the most attractive and squirrel-like of all the Central American rats, is a tawny-coloured tree-dweller with an almost bushy tail. The animal builds neat little nests of shredded bark high up in the tall trees, where it lives in colonies. It rarely comes down to the ground, for there is food aplenty for it in the trees; it is especially fond of the fruit of the avocado tree and wild figs.

The American Harvest Mouse, *Reithrodontomys*, is not really a harvester, as you might suppose it to be. This dainty creature comes by its name through being found in the fields when crops are gathered. But it is only there searching for seeds and grass. It looks very much like a house mouse. Seldom over three inches long, it has a slender, finely tapered tail five inches in length.

——A FIRST-RATE BUILDER AND ACROBAT. The harvest mouse is a firm believer in fresh air, and builds its nest in tall grasses. It is fascinating to watch the skill with which this creature constructs its home. It goes to work weaving the grasses into the form of a cup, and tucks in the loose ends with great care. The tiny hands move busily until the cup takes the form of a ball. The little builder uses coarser grasses on the outside to anchor the house securely to the supports. Inside, the dwelling is lined with finely shredded dry grass.

When completed, the nest is a perfect sphere, weather and draught proof; only one little round hole is left open, and this is the door. Sometimes a woodpecker's hole in a tree is chosen as a building site.

Not all harvest mice make their homes off the ground—some prefer to build the dwelling in a depression on the surface or in an underground tunnel. The timid little creatures seldom leave their nests before dark, and are back home again before or soon after sunrise.

At home in its jungle of tall grasses, the harvest mouse is very active, climbing the tall stalks to get at the seeds on top as the stalks sway back and forth in the breeze. From this dizzy height it will swing itself like an acrobat to other swaying grasses. As it climbs, its long tail helps it to maintain its balance.

——BUGLE CALL OF THE HARVEST MOUSE. The harvest mouse usually breeds twice a year. The height of the mating season comes in April and September. During this time, the male gives voice to a shrill, bugle-like song—it is very faint and in a key almost too high for the human ear.

From three to seven helpless babies are born about twenty-four days after mating time. These mites may weigh as little as one-twentieth of an ounce and are naked and blind. Their eyes open, and they get their first teeth, in about eight days. They are weaned when two weeks old, and ten days later they are on their own. Fully grown at about five weeks of age, they will weigh about a third of an ounce or more.

By the time the young mice have been running about their native fields or meadows three months or so, they must start raising their own families. Time is short in the harvest mouse's world; at the end of a year the animal is quite old.

The American harvest mouse is a field mouse of the western United States, but has extended its range across the Mississippi into South Carolina, Virginia, and Florida; southward, it spreads through Mexico and Central America to Ecuador. There are about seventy different kinds, but their habits and general behaviour are much the same. Their colour varies on the back from dark brown to buff, with white or pinkish-white under-parts.

The White-footed Mouse, *Peromyscus,* makes its home in many different parts of North America, and when an animal gets around as much as this one does, it acquires a good number of names. The white-footed mouse is called the "wood mouse" because it lives in the woods, the "deer mouse" because of the deer-like colour of its fur, and the "vesper mouse" because it comes out in the evening. A Florida white-footed mouse even lives in the holes of the gopher turtle, and for that reason is known as the "gopher mouse". We will frequently find Mr. White-Foot climbing up a tall tree, but more often we see him scurrying across the ground.

The white-footed mouse will make its nest almost anywhere so long as the spot is warm and dry. A hollow tree is the place it likes best, but a vacated squirrel nest or bird nest will also serve its purpose. In the winter it has been discovered in a beehive along with the bees. On the prairies some of these creatures dig burrows. The author, on periodic short winter visits to his country place in Connecticut, has found white-footed mice snug and warm in a mattress and in bureau drawers, but when he makes a protracted stay in the spring, they usually move out.

No matter where these little creatures live, they have a keen homing instinct; individuals taken prisoner and later released two miles away have been known to return to the place where they were captured.

The white-footed mouse has other remarkable traits as well. It is a musician, and will on occasion indulge in a prolonged buzzing hum. It also makes a drumming sound by tapping its front feet rapidly on some object such as a dry hollow reed or a dead leaf.

IT HUNTS INSECTS IN THE DARK

Note the large ears and lengthy whiskers on the little white-footed mouse—the animal is active at night, and these help it find its way about in the dark. There are scores of different kinds of white-footed mice spread far and wide over North America.

Less appealing is the damage the animal does to crops in fields; it feeds on seeds and nuts. Still, it is not so destructive as its cousin the meadow mouse, and it favours man by eating insects in sizable numbers.

——MOTHER WHITE-FOOT AND HER BABIES. Mice are breeders, and the white-footed member of the family is no exception. The mother produces several litters of one to nine young each year. At birth her babies are blind and bare of fur; they open their eyes for the first time when about two weeks old. From this point on, they develop rather rapidly. They are weaned about a week later, and achieve full growth at ten to twelve weeks of age. They mate when they are eight weeks old.

The mother shows considerable solicitude for her babies. But for the few moments she is out looking for a mate, every moment of her summer is devoted to her children—one litter or the next. Her nest is made of the softest material she can find, and she keeps the entrance closed, so the dwelling is warm and comfortable. If anything seems to threaten the safety of her children, she carries them off one at a time, holding each at the back of its neck with her teeth, to a hastily constructed new retreat.

When the mother is about to have a new family, she does not drive her previous children away from home but moves out herself and builds another nest. This is not an act of unselfishness but a matter of necessity—the old nest is now too contaminated to house newborn babies. The white-footed mouse, though most fastidious about its personal toilet—it continually washes and grooms its fur, keeping its coat spotlessly clean—is not so meticulous in the matter of housekeeping.

——WHITE-FOOTED MICE—AND MORE WHITE-FOOTED MICE. We find some 178 kinds of white-footed mice on the North American continent, from Panama to the Arctic Circle. Most are medium sized, being a little larger than the common house mouse, and have a hairy tail about equal in length to the head and body. Their soft fur is brown or buff on the back and strikingly white below. Their eyes are prominent, round, and black. The ears are large and well developed and the whiskers long—both adaptations of great value to an animal that moves around in the dark.

Closely related to the white-footed mouse is the Lesser White-footed Mouse, *Baiomys*, which we find from southern Texas down to Nicaragua. This drab-coloured creature is only about two inches long, with a tail half an inch shorter. It lives on the ground like the meadow mouse or vole and makes runways through the grass. It is not so likely as some rodents to fight with its own kind. Moreover, there is reason to believe that the male shows affection for his children and helps the mother to watch over them.

The Grasshopper Mouse, *Onychomys,* is also known as the scorpion mouse, but neither the grasshopper nor the scorpion could find any pleasure in having this fierce little rodent as a namesake. For it is out after them every evening, its mouth watering for such delicious morsels.

——A FEROCIOUS HUNTER. Leaving its hole in the ground when the sun has set, the grasshopper mouse stalks its prey on soft padded feet, nose to the ground.

Like the rabbit hound, it gets excited when on a fresh trail, uttering a series of sharp squeaks or barks.

Nothing can deter the grasshopper mouse once it has scented a victim, and it follows the trail at a fast pace. Its beady black eyes sparkle as it comes within striking distance of its game. With a mighty rush, the sturdy little hunter is at its victim's throat; the long, sharp front teeth slash into the brain, and then all is quiet once more.

To all these talents as a hunter the grasshopper mouse adds a virtue —patience. Sometimes it attacks "big game"—for example, a pocket mouse carrying a load of grain—by leaping from an ambush where it has been lying in wait.

Like most creatures of prey, the grasshopper mouse lives a hand-to-mouth existence. When fortune smiles, it feasts royally, but on unlucky nights it starves. It will gorge itself with half its own weight in flesh and blood once a day and will keep this up for weeks when opportunity offers such bounty.

As fearsome as it is to its enemies, this mouse is useful to man. The insects and rodents it destroys are often serious pests, and the gory activity of the grasshopper mouse means considerable savings in pesticides. Only one-tenth of its food is vegetation, seeds and grasses.

——SHARP CLAWS, SHARP NOSE. The grasshopper mouse has many would-be enemies in Nature, but as it lives in a hole underground and is never out hunting before dark, their ravages are cut to a minimum. It is an able digger. Not only does it sometimes excavate its own nest, but also, having located by its keen sense of smell the place where an insect is hibernating below the surface, it claws its way down rapidly and gives the sleeper a rude and final awakening.

In captivity, grasshopper mice show a different side of their character. Now they are gentle and quite friendly to each other. But they will protest when they are handled, showing their resentment with a bite from their sharp teeth.

——Babies Weighing One-Tenth of an Ounce. Life starts slowly for the new grasshopper mouse, but soon increases its tempo. The first young of the year come about April or May. There are four or five naked, sightless babies in the family, and they weigh only about one-tenth of an ounce each at birth. They do not open their eyes before they are two weeks old, but they are out feeding themselves in another ten days. Now let all small things that creep and run and hop beware; there are more appetites abroad, and they are mighty ones!

——Grasshopper Mice North and South. There are two major groups of these rodents. The typical Grasshopper Mouse, *Onychomys leucogaster*, is a sturdy, medium-sized mouse with a comparatively short tail. The back and the top of its head are buff; the rest of the soft, silky fur is snow-white. We find this mouse in western North America from British Columbia and Saskatchewan south to northern Mexico. The Scorpion Mouse, *Onychomys torridus*, is smaller and has a bright tawny coat and longer tail. It makes its home in the hot, arid deserts of the south-west.

——When Winter Comes. The grasshopper mouse does not hibernate even in the coldest part of its territory. Its body and tail usually become especially fat and plump in the autumn and it does make some efforts to store up food for winter use. When the weather is exceptionally cold, the animal may stay at home for a week or more and draw sustenance and energy from its stored-up fat and the seeds it has laid up.

The Cotton Rat, *Sigmodon*, was so named in the southern United States because of the balls of cotton found along its runways after it had dined on cotton seeds. It is a medium-sized, robust rat with a tail usually shorter than its head-and-body length, and it has short, broad ears. Its hair is moderately long, coarse, and grizzled, or finely mixed buff and black.

The cotton rat is at home not only in the southern United States, but also in Mexico, and as far south as Venezuela to Peru. Active during the daytime, this creature may be seen in many different types of country. It frequents wet meadows, dry fields, cultivated land, salt marshes, and tidewater flats, and may even be encountered high in the mountains.

This rodent does not feed exclusively on cotton seeds. It will eat most kinds of edible vegetation but favours grass, sedges, and the roots of succulent plants, which it digs out of the wet earth. Unable to climb, it gets at fruit and seeds by cutting off the plants near the bottom; they will not fall in a dense meadow, and so the rat pulls them down within reach. It also devours quantities of insects, eggs, and crabs.

The cotton rat is a great quarreller, and its arguments often end in cannibalism. An injured or trapped animal will be promptly consumed by its fellows, and a female may even kill and devour an over-zealous suitor.

——A PROLIFIC FEMALE. The female, bloodthirsty as she is, is much more remarkable as a giver of life. She has an extreme reproductive capacity when there is an ample supply of attractive food. She breeds frequently in the warm southern states and each litter contains four or more babies; a few hours after their birth she will mate again. The next brood comes in twenty-seven days and, if there is plenty of food, more babies follow quickly.

Not only does the mother have large families, but she will permit several previous generations to stay in the home nest.

The retreat of the cotton rat may be in an underground tunnel or in a shallow depression in the ground. The nest is made from dry grass and root fibres, and in the cottonfields a cotton rat may collect a peck of cotton to line it.

Females often mate when only seven weeks old and there is much interbreeding between close relatives. The mating season extends from February to November; it may be continuous the year round under favourable conditions.

Five hundred cotton rats to an acre is not very unusual in cultivated areas. You can readily see that its great numbers make this rodent a serious menace to crops. The cotton-rat population suffers periodic setbacks every four or five years, when the animals are attacked by a fungus disease that sweeps through their hordes and eliminates whole colonies. In six months or a year, however, new stock moves in and the process of fast multiplication is on again.

The Wood Rat, Pack Rat, Trade Rat, or Cave Rat, *Neotoma*, is a rodent famed in tales of the North American West because of its unusual habits. It has a compelling desire to collect unusual objects, and keeps them in a little "museum". In its treasure house you may find such things as nails, coins (sometimes stolen from the pockets of sleeping people), bits of tin, coloured glass, china, rags, bleached bones and skulls, eyeglasses, and false teeth.

——A RODENT TRADER. Closely associated with this acquisitive instinct is the wood rat's habit of "exchanging" articles. In rifling the pockets of a sleeping person, the wood rat will leave behind a few nuts or a pine cone. On one occasion, according to an oft-repeated tale, a wood rat left some gold nuggets on the table in a prospector's cabin in exchange for some trivial trinkets. By following the animal's trail, the prospector found his fortune in a rich gold-bearing vein.

——THE WOOD RAT'S "CASTLE". Although the wood rat is most numerous along the backbone of the continent in the Rocky Mountain region, its range extends from the Atlantic to the Pacific, from Nicaragua northward, though not so far as the Hudson Bay and Great Lakes regions. It inhabits cliffs, caves, open woodland, and arid regions.

The wood rat is a home-lover and takes great pains with its "castle". On the Pacific coast the house may be five or six feet high and have one or two rooms. In general, it is a globular affair of sticks and grasses built in a cavity among the rocks, in a hollow tree, in the branches of a tall tree, or in a cactus growth. The inside is lined with soft shredded bark or grass. Since the nest is a permanent home, the animal enlarges and improves it from time to time.

Like the squirrel, the wood rat hoards large quantities of seeds, grain, and nuts in the autumn for food during the winter, laying them up in a storeroom. A most fastidious housekeeper, the animal has a place for everything, including a regular garbage dump for refuse.

While the wood rats are sociable in the sense that they live in colonies, they do not visit one another's homes though there are well-worn community trails. Active mostly by night, these rodents feed on vegetable matter, which includes greens and all food of this nature. Some greens are put out on rocks to dry and cure before being taken home to the storehouse.

A number of the wood rats drink considerable amounts of water, but others that live out on the desert have little use for it; they get their liquid from the pulpy cactus flesh and succulent root tubers.

——A LONG JOURNEY, A HARSH GREETING. The wood rat breeds once or twice during the year. The male gets restless in January and makes

CURIOSITY IS ITS MIDDLE NAME

Most appealing of the large family of mouse-like rodents
is the golden hamster. A fairly recent import to America
from Eurasia, this chubby, friendly little animal with its inquisitive, acquisitive nature has been widely accepted as
a pet in the United States. The soft thick fur covers even
the soles of its feet so it is truly "quiet as a mouse".
See page 318.

L. G. Kesteloo—Va. Comm. of Game and Inland Fisheries

THE MUSKRAT—AN OVERGROWN MEADOW MOUSE

The muskrat, a close relative of the meadow mouse, is another rodent very much at home in the water. Its hind feet are webbed; it has thick fur that sheds moisture, and a vertically flattened tail which it uses as a rudder. The muskrat lives in a hole in the bank of a stream, or builds itself a dome-shaped house of mud and rushes. This animal possesses glands which emit a musky odour.

See page 322.

nightly trips beyond the usual home territory, in search of a mate. Sometimes he travels half a mile or more. Having found a likely prospect, he proceeds with caution. Even though he may be acceptable to the female, she will not be won without considerable sparring. Her temper may break out at any moment, and an over-persistent suitor may get a split ear or a wounded tail for his trouble.

However, a successfully mated couple of wood rats will remain together longer than most rodents during courtship. The male may be tolerated in the home even after the young are born. They come, two to six of them, about four weeks after the mating, and each weighs about half an ounce. Weaned at three weeks of age, they begin to forage for themselves. The mother takes good care of them, and may allow them to stay with her when they can already find their own food.

——A DRUMMER AND A CHIRPER. While the wood rat is not credited with unusual vocal powers, it will thump on the ground with both hind feet when alarmed, or vibrate the tip of its tail rapidly up and down. When it taps on dry leaves, the noise will carry a considerable distance; it probably serves as a danger signal. Like any rat, when seized by an owl or other foe it will give out a desperate shriek. Occasionally, during the mating season, it has been heard to make low chirps.

The bushy-tailed rats of western North America are the most attractive of the wood rats; indeed, with their deep, soft fur, they are more like squirrels than rats. Large ones will weigh up to one pound or more and measure nine inches in head-and-body length, with a tail about an inch shorter. Such a rat will stand about three inches at the shoulder.

All told, there are twenty-eight species, with some close relatives in Mexico.

The Fish-eating Rat, *Ichthyomys*, and several closely related smaller water mice dwell in the mountains of tropical America, from Honduras south to Peru. They are rodents that have to a certain extent turned away from the tribe's traditional habit of feeding on seeds and vegetable matter and have gone a-fishing or a-hunting.

We know little about these strange creatures. The naturalist Stirton, however, has observed some in El Salvador. He found them in streams at the bottom of deep canyons, with heavy cloud-forest vegetation on both sides, and with only tiny spots of sunlight on the dripping fronds and moss-covered walls. Large oaks were laden with orchids, and other plants overhung the banks.

The fish-eating rats also frequent the countless crystal-clear streams that plunge down the mountain slopes through the damp forests at elevations between three thousand and eleven thousand feet. By night, the animals swim about in the rock-bound pools and scramble over partly submerged tree trunks in search of salamanders hiding behind stones, or water beetles concealed in dark corners.

These rodents often have a strong fishy smell when captured, and we assume that occasionally one will catch and eat small fish, but we have no direct evidence of this. Of seven animals examined by Stirton, three *Neusticomys*, or fish-eating mice, had fed bountifully on beetles, freshwater snails, crustaceans, and mussels. Three of the fish-eating rats of Ecuador, *Anotomys*, had been eating some kind of mammal, and had considerable hair in their stomachs but no bones. This hair apparently came from one of their kind, suggesting cannibalism. Feathers of what was probably a wren, and the skin and bones of a salamander, were also found in a water mouse, *Rheomys*, in El Salvador.

The fish-eating rat, *Ichthyomys*, is the largest and handsomest of the five known kinds. It is about the size of a large house rat— seven inches long, with a hairy tail almost as long again—and has small ears. Especially adapted for life in the water, it possesses soft, dense fur and glossy overhair, which serves to keep the animal warm and dry as it moves along in a chilly stream or pool. Its hind feet are greatly enlarged for swimming, and are fringed with stiff hairs. It is glossy greyish black above and silvery grey below. Literally, its scientific name means "fish mouse".

HAMSTERS—BURROWERS OF THE OLD WORLD

Hamsters are fat, chubby, little animals with thick, soft fur. They have short limbs and a little bobbed tail. You cannot hear these creatures as they patter about at night, for the soles of their feet are well padded with hair. They possess large cheek pouches in which they transport grain.

The hamsters are great hoarders. Thus we are not surprised to learn that in Central Europe the word "hamster" is used to signify selfishness or a greedy person. The name, however, once had a different meaning. It came from an Old High German word, *hamastro*, meaning "weevil". Like that insect, the hamster is a borer, but mainly under the ground, where it lives in tunnels.

Although tame hamsters have achieved a great vogue in the United States in recent years, they are not native to the New World. The common hamster we see in pet shops today is the descendant of animals imported from south-eastern Europe and south-western Asia. In the wild, hamsters are better known in Europe than elsewhere, but they are also plentiful over most of northern Asia.

The European Hamster, *Cricetus*, is the largest of the hamsters— it is about a foot long. Its fur is very thick, with a typical colour pattern: light brown on the back, with white and red markings on the sides. The animal's under-parts are black.

This is odd, in a way, for it is the reverse of the usual natural colour scheme. Other animals are nearly always dark above and light below. The light under-colours tend to eliminate a perceptible shadow on the under-side of the animal, and so help it to escape detection. In this hamster, however, the shadowed under-parts are greatly emphasized by the black.

The European hamster frequents farm lands in eastern Europe and western Asia. It is common in grass fields and cultivated areas but shows a preference for dry, sandy soil in which to dig its labyrinth of subterranean runways. The entrance to the den, or "creeping hole" as it is called, is marked by a large pile of excavated earth. The animal makes its runways about two inches in diameter and digs them on several levels. Conveniently, all lead to the central nest chamber, two or three feet below the surface.

——FOOD FOR A RAINY DAY. Under cover of darkness the hamster sallies forth in search of plunder. It digs up potatoes and tears down stalks of wheat and oats to get at the grain on top. Food is not eaten on the spot but borne home to the underground storehouse. The hamster carries potatoes and other tubers between its front teeth; it stuffs wheat and other grain in its cheek pouches until they are filled to capacity. Home at last, and ready to unload, it empties the pouches partly by blowing, partly by pressing with its forefeet on its cheeks.

No matter how well fed the hamster may be, its natural instinct urges it to collect food for a rainy day. One hamster storeroom may contain as much as a whole bushel of grain besides quantities of roots. The food is kept in good condition, and is not permitted to rot with dampness; the hamster stores the potatoes and root crops separately from the grain. There is a place for everything, and everything must be in its place, in the pantry of this surprisingly clean, methodical creature. In addition to the foods already mentioned, the European hamster will eat beets and fallen apples. However, it is not just a vegetarian, but kills and eats small animals and birds and their young.

——SLEEPY TIME. In the autumn the hamster gets fat, and, with its storehouse now well filled, stays home in the nest most of the winter. It may reach a dormant state but apparently it does not go into complete hibernation. Early in the spring, the animal moves to a new location and digs a fresh burrow in which to live during the coming summer.

This hamster will breed four or five times during the year. Usually it bears families of from five to twelve young, but sometimes there are as many as eighteen babies in a litter. The infants make no great demands upon their parents' patience: two weeks after birth they have left home and each is setting up housekeeping in a burrow of its own.

——FIGHTING THE HAMSTER. Because of the damage it does to crops, the European hamster is hunted by the farmer. Sometimes he uses dogs to kill it, and sometimes he floods the burrows with gas. However, the cornered hamster is a courageous fighter and will not hesitate to spring at either dog or man; there is a record of one hamster that seized a horse by the nose when the animal stepped on its burrow.

In defending itself, the hamster will make use of its unusual food-unloading practice, already referred to. It will blow the food content of its cheek pouches in the face of an enemy; the points of some seeds strike the foe with such force that they can cause severe pain, making him take to his heels.

Trapped and killed, the hamster yields up a valuable pelt, used particularly to line coats.

Hamsters Around the World. Relatives of the big European hamster are an interesting lot. The Golden Hamster, *Mesocricetus*, is the best known, and one of the most popular pets of the day. It is a golden brown colour and noted for its rapid rate of reproduction; it lives about two and one-half years. Much like it is the South African Hamster, *Mystromys*, the only one found south of the Equator.

Not all hamsters are alike in size. Some of those we find in Asia are no larger than a mouse, and one in Siberia (Miller's Hamster) turns white during the winter. There are hamster moles, with hardly any eyes or ears, and hamsters with manes, in this large group.

VOLES, LEMMINGS, AND MEADOW MICE

Under this popular heading comes a vast army of small, short tailed rodents that far exceed in numbers any other group of mammals found in their particular domain, the cool and temperate regions of the Northern Hemisphere. Grass is the fastest growing and most prolific vegetation on this planet, and the voles and their kin are grass eaters. They are the mills that make the quickest turnover of vegetable matter into flesh and bone to feed a host of hungry meat eaters.

The True Lemming, *Lemmus,* is a chubby little bobtailed vole about six inches in length (only one inch of this is the tail) with long, soft fur completely concealing the ears. Its feet are padded with fur to protect them from the snow and ice. The general colour is a golden yellow brown or buff. On the back of some species we see a dark stripe, while the Scandinavian lemming is very ornate: from the top of the head to behind the shoulders it is glossy black, in sharp contrast with the golden colour of the back.

——STRANGE LEMMING MIGRATIONS. Lemming migrations are one of the wonders of the world. Every now and then the lemming population in a district builds up to enormous proportions. All the food in the region is consumed, and the lemmings must seek fresh pastures. As the little rodents scamper onward, their ranks are swollen by additional bands travelling in the same direction, until thousands of them are on the march.

——A MARCH TO SURE DEATH. Once the animals have started on their traditional pilgrimage, nothing deters them from their course. Not even swift rivers or the sea will halt the hurrying hordes, though death by drowning is certain. The inherited impulse to travel carries them on and on until the multitude dwindles and fades away. Only a few escape, or are left at the starting point, to carry on the race.

During the mass lemming migrations, all the flesh eating birds and mammals—including gulls, hawks, owls, foxes, weasels, bears, cats, wolverines—close in, for here is food for the taking, without the usual hunt or chase. The fish get their share when the lemmings cross rivers and lakes. Even the caribou join in the feast, crushing the little animals between their teeth and swallowing them whole.

The peak of the cycle in lemming population is reached about every fourth year. The migration usually begins in the late winter or early spring and may last a few weeks. But some of the migrations in Norway may continue for a year, the females making short halts to raise a family before moving on again.

——WHY DO THEY DO IT? American Eskimos and peasants of northern Europe have a simple explanation for the sudden appearance of the lemming hordes in their midst. They claim that the animals spiral down from the heavens in a snowstorm. Some of the old Eskimos actually believe that they have seen the creatures falling with the swirling snowflakes.

An equally quaint notion—but this one was begotten by our early scientists—was that when the Scandinavian lemmings migrated, they were seeking their ancient home on the now submerged land of Atlantis. Others have suggested the theory that the lemmings' build-up in numbers is governed by sunspots, but no one really knows the cause.

——THE LEMMING'S HOME. The Brown Lemming, a common little animal of the colder regions of North America, usually constructs a globe shaped nest on the surface of ground more or less covered with moss and vegetation, or burrows beneath a boulder. Soon the nest is filled with five or six babies, the average litter. Under favourable conditions, when the lemmings are building up their numbers before a migration, families may contain as many as eleven; at these times, there is a rapid succession of litters between April and September.

During the long, hard winter, the lemming's nest is covered by a deep blanket of snow. Under it the animal finds ample food and is safe from birds and beasts of prey as well as winter's icy blasts.

Beneath this blanket, too, the lemming is often placed in cold storage by its enemies. The Arctic fox is largely dependent on the little rodent for food, and caches it in large numbers in the icy cold ground as a supply of food for the winter.

The Water Vole, or Water Rat, *Arvicola*, is a familiar figure to every country boy in England. He often sees it sitting up on its haunches along the banks of rivers and ponds nibbling stalks of green vegetation. Sometimes this big brown field mouse (the animal's head-and-body length may be up to eight inches, the hairy tail another four) is found living at a considerable distance from water—too far away for convenient commuting.

The water vole is perfectly at home in the water, has hind feet somewhat adapted for that kind of life (they are not webbed) and is an accomplished swimmer and diver. It is easily tamed and makes a fine pet, but requires plenty of water to swim and bathe in.

——A RODENT SUNBATHER. The water vole is largely active during the hours of light, but may be seen about at any time of the day or night. It feeds almost exclusively on vegetable matter such as duckweed, roots, or water lilies and marigolds. On occasion, however, it will eat small fish, mussels, and freshwater crustaceans. It has an interesting habit of building, among the reeds, little platforms of twigs and cut grasses on which it sits and suns itself.

The home of the water vole is a ball shaped nest of dry grass either in the reeds two or three inches above water level or in a hole in the bank.

There is usually an extensive burrow in the bank; it has an emergency entrance under water. A family generally consists of from five to eight babies. (There are some two litters a year born between April and September.) The mother often carries her children about as a dog does its puppies, transferring them from one dwelling place to another while they are still naked and blind.

——MANY ENEMIES. Moving about on the surface of the water, this small rodent hardly qualifies for the title of a champion swimmer. Under the water it goes faster. Pursued by an enemy, it partly swims and partly runs along the bottom to its emergency hole. As it flees, it raises a cloud of mud that acts as a smoke screen covering its retreat.

The water vole has many foes: otters, stoats, weasels, hawks, owls, and herons are among them. Pike have often been seen taking a water vole, and a large eel was shot while it was swallowing a full-grown one.

——EUROPE'S "MUSKRAT". Though charged with few bad habits, this harmless and rather friendly creature may undermine embankments and dams when excavating its runways. Such offences are never serious and are quite rare.

In many ways the water vole resembles the American muskrat and fills a similar position in Europe. It has a similar thick coat of fur. The flesh of the water vole is a popular dish in some parts of France just as the flesh of the muskrat is in some parts of America.

A native of Europe and most of Asia north of the Himalayas, the water vole is, as we have observed, common in England, but oddly enough it has never reached Ireland. We find a similar situation in Asia; the water vole is common in Siberia yet unknown in China.

The Muskrat or Musquash, *Ondatra,* is North America's most valuable fur bearer in point of the total number of skins used. Trappers take between ten and twelve million muskrats every year and so their pelts have become among the cheapest on the wholesale market.

In the trade the processed fur reappears under elegant names. You

A VALUABLE FUR-BEARER

The muskrat is highly esteemed for its fur, which, when dressed, looks somewhat like that of the fur seal. Muskrats are extensively trapped, but they are in no danger of being wiped out; the animals are prolific breeders, and it is not uncommon for a single female to bear over thirty babies a year.

will often meet it as Electric Seal, Near Seal, Bisam Mink, Hudson Seal, Hudsonia, Loutrine, River Sable, River Mink, and Water Mink. The muskrat, however, is none of these exotic creatures, but a humble rodent that dwells near swamps, lakes, and streams, over the greater part of the continent, from the northern tree limit south to the Mexican border.

——WHY IT LIVES THERE (INDIAN VERSION). The American Indians have a colourful legend to explain how the muskrat came to occupy the haunts in which we find it today. They say that once it aided Nanabojou, their sun god, during a great flood. As a reward for this good deed, he gave the animal the choice of living in any part of the country it wished. The muskrat was so enchanted by the deep blue lakes that it chose to dwell there.

Alas, the muskrat, it seems, is a fickle creature—or this one was, at any rate. Soon it was back in the god's presence, asking to be given the grassy banks instead. Kindly Nanabojou complied with its wishes.

The following day, however, Nanabojou's patience was sorely tried when the muskrat reappeared, this time to complain that it had nowhere to swim in its new home: it wanted to be returned to the lakes.

Said Nanabojou: "One day you want land and the next you ask for water. Since you do not know your own mind, I shall decide for you. Henceforth your home will be in the marsh, the borderland that is neither dry land nor open water. Here you will have long green grass to eat and water deep enough to swim in."

This proved to be just what the muskrat wanted, and it has lived in such places until this day. There, to dwell in, it often digs a hole in the bank, with the entrance under water, or else it builds itself a house of reeds and grasses out in a pond or lake, but always in shallow water.

——A DUAL PURPOSE HOUSE. House building with the muskrat is not an engineering achievement, as it is with the industrious beaver. In fact, the house is a shoddy piece of construction, although, as we shall see, it has a twofold purpose.

The muskrat first heaps up rushes and reeds until it has made a pile that reaches well above the water line. It then chews out a cavity in the middle of a nest chamber with an underwater entrance. Additional material is stacked on the pile from time to time. Although in other seasons it eats herbs, grain, and water animals, in winter, when everything is frozen hard and food is scarce, the muskrat sits at home and feeds on the inner walls of its house.

Muskrats breed throughout the summer, from April to September. Two to six babies come about a month after the adults mate. In another month the youngsters are able to find food on their own, and their mother's sharp teeth show them they must be on their way; she has to get ready for another brood.

——A BIG MEADOW MOUSE. Weighing two or three pounds, and about ten inches in head-and-body length (the scaly tail is half as long again), the muskrat is smaller than the beaver—actually, it is just an overgrown meadow mouse, made for a life in the water. Its hind feet are broad and partly webbed for swimming. Its thick, soft fur is waterproof, and is overlaid with long, oily, reddish brown guard hairs which enable it to shed moisture. Its tail, vertically flattened, is an efficient rudder.

——HOW THE MUSKRAT GOT ITS NAME. The muskrat got its name from the musky secretion of the perineal glands. The odour is not unpleasant, and the secretion is sometimes used in the preparation of perfume.

These animals are in general inoffensive, so far as man is concerned. Sometimes, however, the muskrat does cause some trouble, as in Europe, where it has been introduced. In some places it undermines dikes and dams as it pursues the inclinations of a burrower. In North America its chief enemies are the minks, snapping turtles, hawks, and eagles.

——FLORIDA'S MUSKRAT. Florida has a muskrat all its own. This one, not over eight inches in head-and-body length, is even more like an overgrown field mouse than is the common muskrat. It has a round instead of a flat tail, and is known as the Round tailed Muskrat, or Florida Water Rat, *Neofiber*. As the scientific name suggests, it belongs to a different genus.

The Pine Mouse, *Pitymys*, was so named because it was first discovered in the pine forests of Georgia, in the United States, probably on the LeConte plantation near Riceboro. Like so many other animals' names, this one's is misleading; pine trees are not necessarily a part of the pine mouse's homeland; open meadows and pastures provide an equally suitable setting for the animal's activity. Nor is the creature found only in Georgia—we meet it in other eastern states, and in Mexico as far south as Veracruz, as well as in continental Europe and Asia.

The pine mouse is a small rodent, very similar in general appearance to a meadow mouse but more or less modified for a life under the ground. The American pine mouse has very close soft brown fur, small eyes, and reduced ears.

This rodent digs long, shallow tunnels and pushes up the displaced soil into small mounds of earth. It feeds on tubers and will clean out a field of potatoes, leaving no visible trace of its raids except the dead potato tops. Moles are often blamed for the damage done to bulbs and roots by the pine mouse.

——GREAT DAMAGE DONE BY THE PINE MOUSE. Given a fast growing root crop, the pine mouse is capable of rapid mass reproduction. Its numbers will multiply sufficiently to consume many acres of available potatoes in a short time. In a field of potatoes in Connecticut completely destroyed by these mice, the author found every row honeycombed with runways; when he started to dig, he could see many of the mother mice running away over the surface, their babies dangling from their mouths as the parents carried them to safety.

Once the harvest was over, these hordes of Connecticut mice were confronted with only a normal supply of food, not nearly enough for such quick breeders. They turned to other fields for sustenance. Some young orchard trees close by had their entire root systems devoured by the hungry pine mice, and the first high wind blew the trees clean out of the ground.

The Common Field or Meadow Mouse, or Vole, *Microtus*, one of the most abundant of all rodents, is an inoffensive, drab-coloured creature only three or four inches long. It is not especially attractive— just a ball of long, soft fur, two little sparkling black eyes, and a short tail.

Despite its small size and humble appearance, the common meadow mouse plays an important role in the lives of many larger animals and birds. An almost endless array of appetites depend on it for satisfaction: the meadow mouse is food for cats, lynxes, skunks, weasels, martens, fishers, minks, opossums, dogs, foxes, coyotes, wolves, badgers, black bears, grizzlies, and brown bears, as well as many kinds of hawks, owls, eagles, crows, jays, magpies, seagulls, snakes. This is not nearly the end of the list—even fish and snapping turtles get their share of meadow mice.

But for the industrious reproductive habits of the meadow mice, there would not be nearly enough of them to go around. Their breeding season is almost never closed; there are young in the nest almost all the year round. A single female may produce as many as seventeen litters of four to nine young (sometimes as many as thirteen) during one year. The babies are born naked, blind, and helpless, about three weeks after mating time; two weeks later they are weaned and on their own. The nest, a globe-like shape of woven grasses, may be hidden in a depression in the ground or under an old log. Sometimes it is underground.

——THE SHORT-LIVED MEADOW MOUSE. The meadow mouse expends a tremendous amount of energy in an apparently endless round of day

THE MOUSE THAT LIVES A YEAR

The common field mouse is short-lived—indeed, only the hardiest will survive longer than a year. One reason is that it furnishes food for many larger animals and birds. Another is that this minute creature devours its own weight in grass and seeds every day, and it wears itself out in the never-ending hunt for food.

and night activities. It consumes its own weight in food every twenty-four hours and so it must always be searching for the leaves, seeds and grasses it needs to keep itself going. Plants make up most of its diet, though it will eat some insects and meat.

With its constant hunt for food, its constant breeding, small wonder that the life fires of the meadow mouse are burned out before its first birthday comes around. Some doddering old males may live eighteen months, but few ever reach that old age.

——MEADOW MICE GALORE. The nervous little meadow mouse has never been satisfied to stay just in meadows. We find it in all kinds of places, hot and cold, high and low—in swamps and woods, on plains and prairies, from sea-level to mountain tops. From place to place, it has many different forms—there are 238 types of meadow mice named, including many subgenera. They have an enormous range in the Northern Hemisphere, including all North America from Alaska south to Guatemala, all Europe, and northern and central Asia, and Asia Minor.

——MOUSE PLAGUES. The ancients knew the meadow mouse well. If you have read Greek literature, you are probably familiar with the worship of the Mouse God Apollo. Apollo was looked upon as the instigator of the various mouse plagues from which Greece suffered. It is easy to understand the reverence in which the old Greeks held his powers, for food was scarcer then than now, and a mouse plague might destroy an entire year's crops, bringing hunger to whole countrysides.

Even in our own time a mouse plague is no laughing matter. Under favourable conditions, especially in Europe, the meadow mouse multiplies in an incredible manner. There are many instances where harvests over large tracts of land have been completely destroyed during what is known as a "vole year". Fortunately, when the meadow mouse or vole population has reached a high peak, they have a plague of their own and their numbers are quickly reduced below normal.

SOME OTHER CURIOUS MICE AND VOLES

The Snow Mouse or Collared Lemming, *Dicrostonyx*, lives farther north than any other rodents; it dwells in Asia and North America, and makes its home under the ground. With the exception of a small Asiatic hamster, it is the only rodent that changes from a brown summer coat to a snow-white one in winter.

Another curiosity of the snow mouse is that it is the only mammal that sheds its toe-nails annually. The third and fourth claws on the front feet grow excessively long and broad in winter and are replaced by normal claws in April or May. The animal may or may not have a tawny band across its throat.

THE MOUSE THAT IMITATES THE ERMINE

The snow mouse, which lives in the colder parts of Asia and North America, is the only mouse that wears a white coat in winter, a brown one in the summertime. This animal lives underground, and in the winter makes runways in the snow. It grows longer claws at this time, possibly for digging in the ice and snow.

Relic of the Ice Age? For a number of years the skulls of a strange mouse with broad, grooved front teeth kept turning up in owl pellets in populated districts like New Jersey, but no naturalist could find where the owls got them. Eventually one labelled "Hoboken, New Jersey", turned up in a museum collection.

This rare and elusive vole is now known as the Lemming Mouse, *Synaptomys*, and lives largely in cool, moist swamps and bogs in north-eastern North America. It is not to be confused with the lemming, though it has much the same habits, including the urge to migrate. Some scientists consider it a hangover from the Ice Age; they believe it was left behind in cool sphagnum bogs and on shaded mountain slopes when the ice retreated north.

A Handsome Little Brownie. One of the comeliest little denizens of the English countryside is the Bank Vole, *Clethrionomys*. It is a pretty, furry little creature with a broad splash of reddish-brown colour down the middle of its back. Known as the Red-backed Mouse in the United States, this tiny brownie favours the northern belt of evergreen forest that encircles the globe. It follows no beaten trail but trots along the forest floor scrambling over fallen logs, and even climbs trees.

A Vole That Lives in Trees. While practically all the voles make their living on the ground and rarely climb trees, the Red Lemming, *Phenacomys*, has reversed the order—it lives in the trees and rarely descends to the ground; for this reason it is often referred to as the Tree Lemming.

The red lemming feeds on the fleshy wood and needles of the Douglas and Grand firs in the Rocky Mountains. Its nest, sometimes thirty feet above the ground, consists of twigs and pine needles. Unlike all the other voles, this one has the long tail of a tree-dweller. (However, many of the species actually have short tails and never climb trees.) It also differs from other members of its tribe in having a slow rate of reproduction, usually two in a litter, which do not leave the nest until a month old.

It Digs With Its Teeth. The Mole Lemming, *Ellobius*, of Asia Minor and Central Asia is the subterranean member of the voles. The claws on the front feet are not especially large for a burrower, but the long, powerful front teeth projecting beyond the closed lips are a fair compensation. This novel specialization enables the animal to hack away at the earth with its teeth without getting its mouth full of soil, just as the beaver keeps its mouth dry when cutting wood under water.

GERBILS—RATS OF THE OLD WORLD DESERTS

Gerbils are the typical small mammals you will encounter if you travel across the desert regions and sandy wastes of Asia, Africa, and southern Russia. Here, in the hottest and driest parts of the world, these animals often live many miles from water.

A burrow, excavated in the sand, is the gerbil's home. The animal may be sociable and share community tunnels or else lead a solitary life; male and female usually do not nest together. In Russian Turkestan the author saw a dozen or more of them, the Sand Rats, *Meriones*, that appeared to be chasing one another around in sport. They kept it up until he came within twenty or thirty yards of them, whereupon all dived into their holes. These seemed to constitute a common network of underground burrows.

Most of the gerbils are about only during daylight hours. They feed on seeds, grasses, and roots, which for the most part contain a little moisture. There are quite a number of different kinds of gerbils, the majority about the size of a house rat. Largest of all is the Great Sand Rat, *Rhombomys*; at home in central Asia, the Caspian Sea region, and Mongolia, this creature has surprisingly thick fur for a hot-country animal. Usually gerbils are protectively coloured like the desert sands in which they live, and have large ears so that they can hear sounds from afar.

——JUMPERS OF THE DESERT. Often the gerbils are called "antelope rats" because of the way they move about. Their hind legs are fairly long, and they hop rather than scamper or scurry in typical rat fashion. In this respect they remind us of the jerboas, or jumping rodents; indeed, "gerbil" is just another form of the name "jerboa".

BUILT FOR BURROWING

The mole lemming, found in Central Asia and Asia Minor, is the vole that goes underground. Its remarkable digging powers are chiefly due to the projecting front teeth—yet the lemming mole's specially adapted lips prevent its mouth from filling with soil.

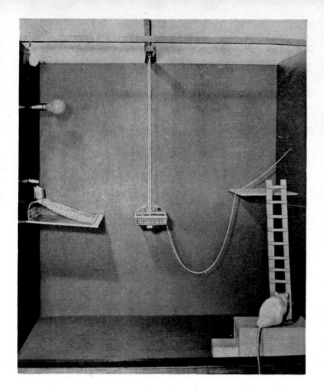
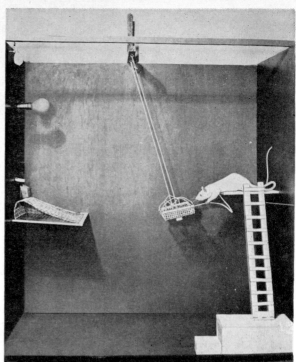

Freelance Photographers Guild

IT "SWINGS" FOR ITS SUPPER

White mice are famous for their part in laboratory studies of behaviour patterns. This one quickly learned to climb the ladder, draw the basket to the platform, jump in and ride across to the other side where it finds food. Derived from a parent stock of common house mice by careful breeding, white mice also make interesting pets. *See page 336.*

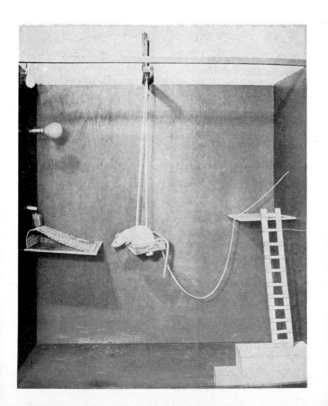

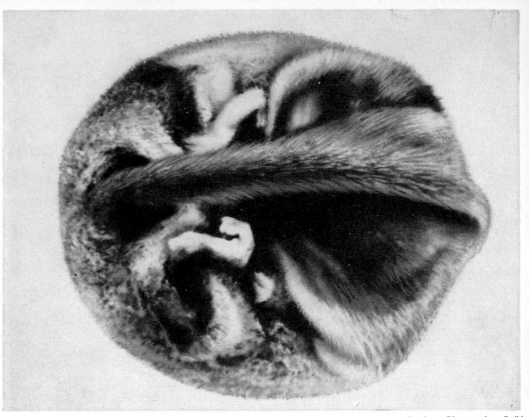

Freelance Photographers Guild

IT HIBERNATES FOR SIX MONTHS

The "dor" of dormouse supposedly comes from the French word "dormir" meaning to sleep, and this the dormouse does for months at a time. Like all true hibernators it does not store food for winter use but grows excessively fat in the autumn, then sleeps soundly throughout the hibernation period, drawing what little sustenance it needs from the fat. *See page 343.*

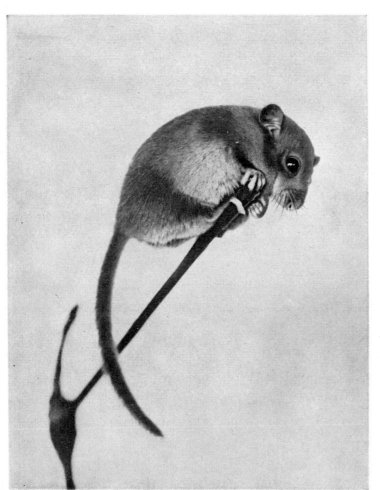

POPULAR BUT MYSTERIOUS

While it resembles the squirrels not only in appearance but habits, spending most of its life in the trees and feeding on acorns, seeds and fruit, the dormouse sleeps by day and roams abroad at night. It is seldom seen, and even in the sections of the Old World where it lives it is best known for its role in "Alice in Wonderland." *See page 343.*

Freelance Photographers Guild

OLD WORLD RATS AND MICE—AND
THEIR NEW WORLD DESCENDANTS

Just as America owes its first white settlers to the Old World, so does it owe its population of house mice and rats. They were fairly early settlers, too—they arrived in the United States at the time of the American Revolution. The conflict they started, however, has long outlasted that one.

The scurrying legions of domestic mice and rats form only two small branches of a huge rodent family, the Muridae (the name comes from the Latin word *mus*, "mouse", and old Linnaeus, who pretty much set the style in the scientific naming of animals, applied it to all rats and mice). Although this group was originally limited by the shores of the Old World, some of its members have penetrated into almost every part of the globe, including many of the islands and even distant Australia, where they developed into true curiosities.

A number of these creatures are genuinely handsome, but most look rather like the familiar rat and mouse, and possess a fairly long, naked tail. By and large they are land animals, with a marked tendency to take to the trees. Given an occasion to enter the water, they generally show that they can swim well.

The Dwarf Mouse, or Old World Harvest Mouse, *Micromys minutus,* is one of the great acrobats of the mouse world. It looks as

TINY GATHERER OF THE HARVEST

The dwarf mouse or harvest mouse of the Old World searches for seeds and grass in the fields at harvest time. A talented acrobatic performer, this small rodent has a long tail (half of the over-all length of five inches) by which it may suspend itself while it engages in its antics. The mouse shown above is resting on its ball-shaped nest.

though it were built for its trade, too. Among the smallest of all rodents, it has a slim body that ends in a slender tail about as long as the rest of the animal. The tail is actually prehensile—it can hold on to things. We find this tawny or reddish-brown creature spread from Great Britain and continental Europe east to Japan.

The dwarf mouse loves to bask in the warm sunlight. It is a great performer and takes its exercise in the daytime, tumbling about on twigs and grass stems, holding on with its tail, which it sometimes wraps twice around a twig or grass for a firm hold.

To appreciate the acrobatic antics of this mouse, you should see it on top of a swaying wheatstalk, sitting on its haunches, grooming its tail with both hands. When the wind blows, the mouse rides its "bucking bronco" with great skill. In captivity four or five of these tiny animals will simultaneously perform in a space of six cubic inches, never hitting each other or missing their foothold.

——CRADLE OF THE BABY MICE. The summer nest of the dwarf mouse is a small round ball of cut grass and leaves, about the size of an orange, suspended among reeds or shrubbery about a foot above the ground. It shows no opening, and, when entering, the mouse has to remove a part of the covering. Inside, the dwelling is lined with finely shredded grass and leaves. The nest sways in the wind, and serves as a cradle for the young.

From five to eight babies are born, naked and sightless, about three weeks after mating time. They grow rapidly, and, when about a week old, completely fill the little ball, scarcely leaving room for the mother to crawl inside to feed them. They must soon leave the nest and learn to climb in search of their own food—seeds and insects. There may be two litters in a little more than a month during the height of the breeding season.

In winter, the harvest mouse has a snug, warm retreat in a hedgerow or a hillside, or buries its nest under dense vegetation. During frosty weather, it stays home in its cosy nest but does not hibernate.

The Yellow-necked Mouse, or Old World Wood Mouse, *Apodemus,* is one of the commonest small rodents of Europe; it takes much the same place in the Old World as the white-footed mouse does in the New World. You may find it in forests and wooded country or among rocks, but you will never see it abroad by day. It is strictly a creature of the night.

Although it occurs in a great variety of forms, the wood mouse can generally be recognized by its lengthy tail—this is as long as, or a little longer than, the three- or four-inch body—its large ears, and its big dark eyes. The soft fur is usually some shade of tan or brown with a dark broad band down the back.

——BROAD-MINDED MOTHERS. The wood mouse is a prolific breeder —one pair may raise six families of four or five young during the year. It may locate its nest in almost any place so long as it will be warm, dry, and reasonably safe from its enemies. Several families sometimes are raised in one burrow and in what seemingly is one nest. It is believed that under such circumstances the young do not remain with their respective parents, but accept milk from any one of the mothers that happens to come along.

— –A LESSON FROM THE WOOD MOUSE. Just as the captive lion of fable was aided by a mouse, so were Dutch hyacinth growers by this one. In fact, it gave them a lesson in horticulture.

The growers had noticed that certain hyacinths here and there, instead of blossoming in the usual way, made innumerable bulblets and that in a few years hundreds grew to perfection where there had been only one. Examination of the bulbs when they first failed to bloom revealed that they had been gnawed to the heart by mice. Dutch growers now increase the supply of valuable hyacinths by slashing the bulb to the heart with a knife and cutting numerous cross sections.

——WHERE WE FIND IT. This wood mouse lives in the northern temperate regions of Eurasia, from Ireland to Japan and south to northern India and Mediterranean Africa. Cold weather works no hardship on it—it is active all the winter, but avoids going out during rain and sleet storms.

THE TRUE RATS—A GREAT ARMY

The True Rat, *Rattus*, with its more than 550 recognized kinds, forms a great army which harries man throughout the world. The remorseless rat divisions are made up of creatures of all sizes—there are small ones, only five inches in head-and-body length, looking like overgrown mice; there are large ones, up to a foot in length, that are a fearful sight. The tail is scaly and may even be longer than the rest of the animal.

Rats vary also in their colour and the texture of their hair, which is often grey or brown and sometimes mixed with spines. However, no matter what the variety, you will generally know a rat when you see one—the ratlike form is much the same throughout this huge group.

Man's Close Companion. To man, the house rat is the most objectionable of all living creatures, yet with the exception of the house mouse it is more closely associated with him than any other animal. Wherever man has gone, the rat has followed. It has boarded the ships and travelled to distant lands with him, it has climbed on to the trains and accompanied him inland, and stolen rides on the covered wagons along with the pioneers. It has followed man to war and grown fat on the spoils.

Throughout the years the rat has acquired a liberal education in combating man's efforts to destroy it. To date, it has had the better part of the battle. There are more rats in North America than there are people. They do not accept any meagre dole but annually exact a sizable tribute from the income of every man, woman, and child.

Rats not only thrive in the filth and squalor of city slums and garbage dumps but enter the best of homes and somehow find their way into "ratproofed" warehouses and granaries. Professional exterminators may destroy them by the hundreds, but there are thousands of others ready to move in and take over. They feed on anything edible, even each other if need be.

The Norway Rat, *Rattus norvegicus*, is the common rat found in most cities in the temperate regions, especially in Europe and in the northern United States and Canada. It is also known as the Surmulot, Grey Rat, Brown Rat, Wander Rat, House Rat, or Wharf Rat. Its scaly tail is about equal to the length of its head and body. The animal weighs some one and one-half pounds, but here and there we encounter giants of four pounds.

This rat breeds the year round. It takes roughly three weeks to bring a litter of babies into the world. Under favourable conditions one mother may bear twelve families in one year; six or seven babies come at a time but fourteen are hardly unusual, and there may even be more.

The infants grow rapidly—all too rapidly, one might say. Some rats are ready to breed eight weeks after birth; but three months is the normal age at which they start mating. One and one-half to two years is the limit of a rat's sexual activity, and few ever live to the ripe old age of three.

Another important rat, and very much like the Norway species in its habits, is the Roof Rat, or Alexandrian Rat, *Rattus rattus*. This is the common house rat in the Mediterranean region, the southern United States, Central America, and South America. It is not quite so large as the Norway rat but has a longer tail. Its colour may be greyish brown or black. In South America the black kind is commoner.

Originally the Norway and roof rats were confined to the Old World, but today they are found on every continent and most islands throughout the world. They reached America as stowaways about 1775.

Quarrelsome and Quick to Learn. Rats are usually quarrelsome. Large numbers are often brought together when food is plentiful; on one occasion the author has counted fifty of them in a small hay loft, but it is doubtful that this was a social gathering. Rats learn from the fortunes of their neighbours. A poisoned rat is a recognized warning of concealed danger.

Curious Tales About Rats. There are many curious tales told about rats. Perhaps the oddest is the one that credits them with carrying

UGLY IN ITS LOOKS AND ITS WAYS

The common rat is a city dweller, largely in the temperate parts of the earth. It has always lived close to man, feeding on his supplies and spreading disease among his numbers. The wild mice and rats are quite different from this creature, and often have charming habits, but all have suffered because of their city cousin's reputation.

away hen eggs whole. Eyewitness accounts claim that one rat clutches the egg with all four feet and rolls over on its back; one or two other rats seize hold of the first rat by the tail and drag it away, and even lower it down ladders.

Accounts of such rat egg-wagons have been popular since 1291; the latest is quite recent. All may well be true, as many eyewitnesses claim they are, but perhaps not in the sense they were intended. For one thing, these rat antics have always been observed in dim light, where the imagination works very powerfully. The rat holding the egg may have been trying to keep it from its mates.

The vulnerable part of a rat, we must remember, is its tail, and when one rat attacks another that is what it goes for. The rat holding the egg might permit the others to drag it across the floor by its tail, while it still clung tightly to the booty. Whether the rat would live to enjoy the egg is still another matter.

Great Mother of Rodents. A close relative of the common rat, and one of the most noteworthy members of its clan, is an animal that goes by the singular name of the Multimammate Mouse, *Mastomys*. Usually a female rodent has five pairs of mammae, or teats, but this creature possesses at least eight pairs—sometimes up to twelve pairs. That is more than any other rodent, and probably more than any other mammal except the domestic pig, which may have twenty-eight teats in all.

The multimammate mouse does not allow its exceptional gift to go to waste. On an average she may rear from a dozen babies to a score at a time. Where conditions favour the species, it increases enormously.

Africa is the home of this buffy-brown rat-sized rodent, and it is found in most parts of the continent. It prefers to dwell near cultivated land. Not only does it do great damage to grain crops, but it also carries bubonic plague into human dwellings when the disease is prevalent.

THE COMMON MOUSE—SOMETIMES IT "SINGS"

The Common Mouse, *Mus*, unlike its large relative the rat, is generally regarded by man with contempt rather than with fear. It is a hider and a scurrier, so that its name has come to mean the same as "coward". In older European traditions it was not always held in such low esteem. The mouse was regarded with some dread, and was believed to be the form taken by the soul when it escaped from the lips of a dead person.

Cowardly or not, the common mouse is mighty in its numbers. There are about 130 different kinds, and they vary in size, colour, and length of tail. They originated in Eurasia long ago, but since then they have travelled far. Today we find them all over the world.

The House Mouse, *Mus musculus* (the second scientific name means "little mouse"), is the typical representative of the group. It is indeed a little mouse—only six inches in length, long tail and all. It has soft fur, and this may be brownish grey above and buff on the under-parts. The animal was not known in the New World till about the time of the American Revolution, when, like the rat, it arrived as a stowaway aboard transatlantic ships, and went ashore with the cargo.

The house mouse likes warmth. Established in a heated house, it keeps up a steady increase the year round. There are four to six in normal litters, but at times this is stepped up to nine or ten. They are born about twenty-one days after their parents mate, sometimes later if the mother is nursing a previous litter. The young themselves are ready to breed when two months old.

Snared by a Spider. House mice are active mostly at night. They have many enemies. It is surprising to find that spiders actually snare them. In one instance a black widow spider not only bound a house mouse in its web but administered a lethal bite to subdue its struggles, then ingeniously hoisted the mouse, completely suspending it in the air. There the mouse hung till the spider was ready to eat it.

"Singing Mice". Reports have come from all parts of the world claiming that the house mouse actually sings. Its voice has been described as birdlike in quality but weak, and its song as consisting of a series of pleasing musical chirps and twitters.

When experts have examined the "singing mice" carefully, they have usually discovered traces of abnormal conditions in the nose and throat. They attribute the supposed singing to nothing more than bronchial disorders and asthmatic conditions.

Pests and—Lately—Helpers. All in all, there is little that can be said in favour of the house mouse. Fortunately, it is not suspicious and will walk or run into a trap that would not fool a rat for a minute. The

greater destruction of food by the house mouse is not due to the amount
it consumes, but to the quantity it renders unsuitable for human eating
by contamination with droppings and excrement.

On the positive side, though, domestic house mice are used extensively for experimental medical purposes and in that way have made
valuable contributions to human society. White mice are one of the
breeds that man has produced from the parent stock of the house
mouse.

BANDICOOT RATS—THE "PIG RATS" OF THE EAST

The Bandicoot Rats, *Bandicota* and *Nesokia*, are famous animals in
their homeland of southern Asia, from Turkistan east to Burma and
the Malabar coast. They are no more ratlike in appearance than they
are in habits; their native name, *pandi-kokku*, in the Telugu language
of India, means "pig rat," and was probably applied to them because,
like the pigs, these rats dig in the wet soil for tuberous roots and bulbs,
turning up piles of earth. They are in no way related to the true
bandicoots of the Australian region.

These burrowing rodents are equipped with strong claws and broad
feet for digging in the earth. They have a rather thick, full coat of
fur, soft in some kinds, rather coarse in others. The tail is naked
and scaly, and about equal to the length of the head and body. Most
of these "bandicoots" are about the size of a house rat but the Malabar
Bandicoot (one of the *Bandicota* group) is a giant—it has a head-and-
body length of fourteen inches.

Raiders of the Rice Fields. The bandicoot rats do much damage
in the rice fields of India and Ceylon, besides rooting far and wide for
tuberous roots; they may rob market gardens of yams and potatoes,
but they never enter human habitations.

Creatures of the night, the bandicoot rats visit their favourite feeding
grounds only under cover of darkness. By day they stay in hiding.
Some species live completely underground and, like the American
pocket gopher, push up large mounds of soil.

Family Life Under the Ground. These creatures favour moist
ground as a rule, though the author has found some high up, in the
arid foothills of the Elburz Mountains of northern Iran. Underground,
each animal lives separately, for the bandicoot rats are individualists.

Every one has an extensive set of burrows all its own, dug deep in soft, damp soil. Along one gallery there may be storerooms, which are kept packed with grain, roots, and other food. The nest or den is a circular chamber three or four feet below the surface, lined with leaves, straw, and soft roots or twigs.

It is in this nest that the babies are born. Families of *Nesokia*, it is said, are not large, but little is known about how the young are reared. The female of the greater *Bandicota* has twelve teats, three pairs on the breast and three pairs on the abdomen, to feed the ten or twelve infants she produces in a litter.

At the Mercy of the Tide. These animals are often good swimmers and can travel long distances either on the surface or below water. The author has found bandicoot rats, *Nesokia*, fairly common on the moist plains of Iran along the shores of the Caspian Sea. Their holes were at high-water mark and more or less flooded at times.

The animals seemed to be feeding partly on shellfish and partly on the roots of reeds that grew profusely there. The greatest activity was about the main entrance, where the rats hauled out fresh earth, representing a night's excavating for tuberous roots. Often the creatures walked into traps the author had set up.

These bandicoot rats always left their holes open. Possibly they wanted to be prepared for a quick getaway, should a high tide cover the burrows. That such events happen the writer saw for himself, for one wild, stormy night a high tide not only submerged the bandicoot burrows on the shores of the Caspian Sea with a foot of water but flooded his tent as well. Somehow, the bandicoot rats managed to survive.

The bandicoot rats are often referred to as "pest rats" and are supposed to be host for bubonic and other kinds of fever. Such a charge seems unreasonable in view of the isolated lives of the individuals.

EXTRAORDINARY RATS AND MICE
OF ASIA AND THE PACIFIC

Some Pretty Tree Mice. Even the rats have some attractive relatives. The Long-tailed Tree Mouse, *Vandeleuria*, is a handsome little mouse with a red or bright chestnut coat. It lives in the trees of eastern Asia from Ceylon and India to Indo-China, and feeds on fruits and buds of trees by night; by day it rests in a nest among branches, or in a hollow tree. It is an active little creature, and the long tail is semi-prehensile, serving as an additional hand.

The Marmoset Tree Mouse, *Hapalomys*, of Indo-China has hands like a wee monkey, with an opposable thumb for taking a firm hold of tiny branches and picking up seeds and berries. Its soft, thick fur is brownish grey on the back and snow-white below, and the long tail is tufted at the tip.

Unusual Pests. A rat of economic importance to the people of India and Ceylon is the Coffee Rat, *Golunda*. The attention of Europeans was drawn to this rat when it became a serious menace to the coffee industry—whole plantations were destroyed. The number of these rats once became so great in Ceylon that a thousand were killed in one day on a single plantation.

In New Guinea there is a surprising number of rats. The Mosaic-tailed Rat, *Uromys*, is one of the largest, sometimes being over a foot long in body length. It gets its name from the mosaic pattern of the scales on its tail. Being a big and powerful rat, its booty is the biggest of all nuts; with its chisel-like front teeth this giant can cut through the shell of a coconut.

The natives consider the flesh of the mosaic-tailed rat a great delicacy and hunt it while it sleeps during the day in the fronds of palm trees.

AFRICA'S GIANTS AND PYGMIES

Africa has a fair share of the rats and mice. Some of them are quite attractively marked. One species, the Striped Grass Mouse, *Lemnisomys*, has eight or ten, sometimes fewer, light-coloured lines down the back. The Grass Rat or Kusu, *Arvicanthis*, is represented in thirty-six different forms. It is much like the American Cotton Rat and has rather coarse hair.

Africa's Biggest Rat. The African Giant Rat, *Cricetomys*, a truly enormous creature, measures from twelve to eighteen inches in head-and-body length—with an over-all length of three feet! It frequents the dense thickets and forests of tropical Africa and moves along with measured tread, carrying its tail at an absurd angle in the air. Inoffensive and good-natured, it leads a solitary life, feasting on fruits, seeds and berries.

Tree and Swamp Dwellers. The little African Tree Mouse, *Dendromys*, found south of the Sahara, is as tiny and dainty as the giant rat is great. There is a large group of these so-called tree mice; ornate little animals with one or more dark stripes down the back, they are more apt to be found in the thickets and tall grass than in lofty trees.

The Swamp Rat, *Otomys*, and its relatives are among the commonest rodents of Africa; we meet them from Ethiopia to the Cape. They are the grass-eaters of Africa and are referred to as the "groove-toothed rats". They are about the size of a small house rat.

RODENT ODDITIES OF AUSTRALIA

Rodents That Act Like Marsupials. Rats and mice are among the few placental mammals that reached Australia. Their ancestors probably found their way to this long-isolated land-mass aboard floating trees, or possibly primitive man took them there—unwittingly, to be sure—in his dugout canoes or on his rafts.

The animals have changed greatly since their arrival. We are tempted to suppose that there must be something in the food or air of Australia that makes so many of its animals propel themselves along with a jumping action rather than by running. In any event, a good number of that country's rodents have developed long hind limbs and taken to hopping.

The Australian "Jerboa", *Notomys*, is one of the most interesting— it bounds along like an American kangaroo rat or a true jerboa. It has extremely lengthy ears (we have learned to associate these with the desert, and that is where the animal lives), and a long, bushy tail, which acts as a balancing arm in the jerboa's flying leaps.

Living in a land of marsupials, this rodent seems to have acquired yet another of their habits. Some newborn jerboas, as well as babies of other Australian rodents, have been seen firmly fixed to their mother's teats, clinging to her with mouth and claws as she hopped around in the open.

There are a host of tiny Australian mice, but *Pseudomys*, a delicately coloured, soft-furred creature, is the most attractive. Like the "jerboas", these interesting rodents of the forests and deserts also show a tendency to stand up on their hind legs and hop along.

It Looks Like a Rabbit. Australia has an animal that closely resembles a rabbit—it has long ears and a blunt nose, and sits hunched up like the familiar bunny. Although the settlers called it the "native rabbit", it has long since been named the Nest-building Rabbit Rat, *Leporillus*. And what curious nests it builds!

This odd creature first achieved prominence in 1838, when Mitchell, the Surveyor General, came upon its dwelling places. He found piles of brushwood, which he supposed had been built by the aborigines for signal fires. But, on close examination, Mitchell perceived that the sticks were securely woven together. Inside the pile he discovered a nest of soft grasses, and little animals with big ears and downy fur; they almost impressed him as being baby rabbits, except that the tail was too long.

Each stick house, we have learned, is a family dwelling. These dwellings are grouped together to form little towns, suggesting a social bond and some sort of community activity. The house is well constructed, too. Even Australia's wild dog, the dingo, cannot break in and devour the young.

Australia's Muskrat. The Australian Water Rat, *Hydromys*, a big, glossy, blackish-brown creature with interesting habits, takes the place

WELL EQUIPPED FOR ITS TRADE

A relative of Australia's water rat is the New Guinea water rat, a large animal with webbed feet and a streamlined body. In the water it is almost as agile as an otter, and can overtake fish with ease.

of the muskrat in the Australian region, where it is of considerable economic importance as a fur-bearer.

This animal's home is an elaborate, well-organized castle in the bank of a stream. The bedroom has a soft bunk of finely shredded bark or grass; a nearby compartment serves as a sort of larder or dining room and is usually littered with bones and shells left over from a feast. The front door is under water but there is an emergency exit in the bushes; the living quarters are ventilated by a perpendicular vent hidden in a thicket.

The Australian water rat, on close study, proves itself to be an ingenious fellow. It will roof over the abandoned nest of waterfowl for a summer retreat and will use a flat stone surrounded by water as a dining table. It is a fast swimmer and an efficient diver.

DORMICE—FAMED AS SLEEPERS

Nearly everyone knows the dormouse by name. But who has ever seen one—outside *Alice in Wonderland*, at any rate? What are the facts about this popular but mysterious creature?

First of all, the dormouse is found only in the Old World. Second, it looks more like a squirrel than a mouse. It is covered with very fine, soft, silky fur and has a long, bushy tail. Its round eyes are large and bright.

The dormouse has the ways as well as the pleasing appearance of a squirrel: it spends most of its life in the trees, and is fond of nuts, acorns, and seeds, and, in addition, apples, and other fruits.

The Sleepy Dormouse. The "dor" in dormouse is supposed to come from the French word *dormir*—it means "to sleep"—or an English dialect word "dorm" meaning "to doze". Like many other rodents, the dormouse sleeps through the lean winter season. Often it hibernates as long as six months at a time, and so it has earned a place among the traditional "seven sleepers" of the animal world. (The other six distinguished by this title are the ground squirrel, marmot, hedgehog, badger, bat, and bear, but of course many other animals are winter sleepers, too.)

As autumn draws near, the dormouse gets fatter and fatter. Finally, by October, it is ready to hibernate in a hollow tree or an abandoned birds' nest weatherproofed with moss. Crawling in, it covers over the nest securely, and closes its eyes till spring. Unfortunately, its foe the weasel does not feel tired at all while the dormouse slumbers, and often pulls it from its cosy dwelling.

Young Dormice—Not So Sleepy. The dormouse breeds twice a year—once in the spring, and again in the autumn. About three weeks after mating, the female bears two to four infants. Although they cannot do much for themselves at first—they are naked and blind at birth —they mature quickly. They are not fully adult until fifteen months old, or thereabouts. Like many other children the author knows, young dormice do not seem eager to go to sleep. They do not bed down for the winter at the same time as the adults do, but stay active for a while afterward.

THE DORMOUSE—IT LOOKS LIKE A SQUIRREL

This squirrel-like mouse likes to pass its time in the trees, where it finds nuts, acorns, and fruit to satisfy its appetite. It is a deep sleeper—it spends the coldest months of the year slumbering in hollow trees and living off the fat it accumulated in the autumn.

In its waking season, the dormouse is abroad only by night, and that is why it is so little known as a rule. It spends the day sleeping in a nest in the trees. Its life expectancy: six years.

"A Biting and Angry Beast". It is said that the Romans ate a certain species of the dormouse, which they caught in the fat period, before it retired for the winter. The dormouse, as might be expected, had a place in the folklore of Europe during the Middle Ages. In England it was sometimes considered to be as poisonous as a shrew.

Topsell, an old chronicler of animal ways, explains why in his *Four-footed Beasts*:

"If the viper find their (i.e., the dormice's) nest, because she cannot eat all the young ones at one time, at the first she filleth with one or two, and putteth out the eyes of all the residue, and afterwards bringeth them meat and nourisheth them, being blind, until the time that the stomach serveth her to eat them everyone.

"But if it happen that in the meantime any man chance to light upon the viper-nourished blind dormice, and to kill and eat them, they poison themselves through the venom which the viper hath left in them. Dormice are bigger in quantity than a squirrel. It is a biting and angry beast."

Dormice Around the World. In different parts of Europe, Asia, and Africa we find quite a variety of dormice. While they are all medium or small in size, some show interesting adaptations to their surroundings.

The European Dormouse, *Glis*, is the largest, being about the size of a red squirrel. It is not uncommon on the Continent; in some localities large numbers are trapped for the fur trade. A smaller and more attractive species, the Hazel Dormouse, *Muscardinus*, is the reddish-brown little fellow that frequents the hedgerows and woods of England as well as of the Continent.

There are many other members of the dormouse family (Gliridae), but none is more curious to look upon than the Rock Dormouse, *Gliriscus*, which lives in the treeless mountain country of South Africa. This creature has an odd flattening of the skull and body—a specialization that enables it to crawl into narrow crevices in the rocks, where it can be followed by very few enemies.

JUMPING MICE

The Meadow Jumping Mouse, *Zapus*, is also known as the Kangaroo Mouse, and for good reason. It can clear twelve feet in a single leap. Since it weighs less than one ounce, this makes it, relatively speaking, the champion jumper of the mammal world.

Although the meadow jumping mouse has small forelegs, its hind limbs are greatly elongated for leaping. (The mouse's scientific name *Zapus*, literally means "exaggerated foot".) Its tail, twice as long as its three-inch body, serves to maintain the little creature's balance while it is in the air. Oddly enough, it often appears to make its flying leaps at random, without any special landing point in view when it starts.

In other respects, this animal is not very spectacular. Tawny or yellowish brown in colour, it has a broad dark band down the middle of its back. Its feet and under-parts are white or yellowish and it has a spot of black at the tip of its tail.

LITTLE JUMPER OF THE NORTH AMERICAN MEADOWS
Like the kangaroo rat, the meadow jumping mouse has enlarged hind limbs on which it leaps about; the long, slender tail helps it to balance itself while off the ground. At the slightest sign of danger, the mouse goes bounding off in search of safety, often covering twelve feet in a single jump.

The meadow jumping mouse is about in the bright sunlight as well as at night. It does not follow a beaten highway in its search for food, but travels in any direction that appeals to it. A pond will not stop it, for it is a doughty little short-distance swimmer. It feeds on seeds and berries. When blackberries are ripe, its light coloured vest and feet are often stained purple with the juice of the berries.

The jumping mouse usually builds its nest above ground, but if its homeland is a wet, marshy area it may establish its dwelling in grass

[3-13]

Fastidious housekeepers, pack rats have a place for each of the miscellaneous objects they have a penchant for collecting. They never steal, but exchange nuts and pine cones for such treasures as bits of rag, china, and on at least one occasion, false teeth.   *See page 313*

[3-13A]

Rice rats get their name from once having been so numerous in the rice fields of the south-eastern United States. Actually they prefer grass stems to rice, and being much at home in water and marshy ground, found the rice fields excellent for foraging.   *See page 305*

[3-13B]

The furry little red-backed mouse lives all around the globe in the northern evergreen forest. Happily busy with its own affairs, it will even scamper up a tree, although mice in general prefer solid ground.
See page 329

[3-14]

The woodland jumping mouse makes its home in the eastern part of the North American continent, ranging from southern Quebec and Ontario to North Carolina and Tennessee. It spends its days in a burrow dug close to water, moving about at night in kangaroo-like bounds.   *See page 347*

[3-14A]

Another tree-climber, the white footed mouse, will make a home in an abandoned bird or squirrel nest. Although it takes its toll in grain, seeds and nuts, the white foot also performs a great service by devouring sizeable quantities of insects.   *See page 308*

or bushes, where it can stay dry. Winter brings feeding problems with it, and the jumping mouse meets them by spending about six months of the year in profound sleep.

——TIME FOR REST. In preparation for bedtime, the mouse puts on a layer of fat—its only cache of food for the winter. Then it enters an underground burrow below frost line, closes the door securely behind it, and crawls into a comfortable nest of dry grass. It now curls up in a tight little ball, its breathing slackens, and its body temperature declines. To all outward appearances it is dead. The animal remains rigid, cold, and lifeless until the warm breath of spring rouses it to action again.

——BABY JUMPING MICE. The active life of the meadow jumping mouse begins in April, when it comes out of its winter quarters. May is the mating season, and the young are born about thirty days later in a nest underground or on the surface.

There are four or five babies in an average litter, but on occasion we find up to nine nestlings. At birth, they weigh about one-thirtieth of an ounce and look quite unlike their elders. Besides being naked and without sight, they do not even have any whiskers, and their tails are relatively short. After three weeks they see and hear perfectly, and after three more they reach their adult weight of one ounce.

The Woodland Jumping Mouse. In North America the meadow jumping mouse ranges from the Arctic south to California and North Carolina. Its cousin, the Woodland Jumping Mouse, *Napaeozapus*, makes its home from southern Quebec and Ontario down to North Carolina and Tennessee. This creature has a white tip to its tail, and the fur is more yellowish on the sides of its body. As its name implies, it favours forests. Here, not far from water, it digs a burrow, in which it generally passes the daylight hours.

On moonlit nights during the mating season this mouse has been observed behaving in a most unusual manner. It will come out of its hole, bounce around in a sort of erratic dance, collect an armful of nesting material and retreat to its den. In a few minutes the performance is repeated.

These animals have a number of relatives in Europe and Asia (all make up the family Zapodidae), but none matches the Olympic jumping feats of the American branch of the family.

JERBOAS—"KANGAROOS" OF THE OLD WORLD'S DESERTS

The jerboa is another noted leaper of the rodent world, like the jumping mice of the meadows and woodlands, whose ways we have just looked into. In contrast to these animals, the jerboa has chosen as its homeland not only the hottest places on earth, but also the driest and most barren ones.

It loves the arid deserts of the Old World, and appears able to get along completely without water.

Of all the rodents, this kangaroo-like creature is perhaps the most highly developed for getting around on two feet. (As a matter of fact, its family name, Dipodidae, means "two-footed".) Its hind limbs are large and very long. Its front limbs are correspondingly smaller, so that the animal could hardly walk on all fours if it had to.

The jerboa prefers to stand up on its hind legs and hop along, covering from two to six feet in a single jump. Its lengthy tail has a neat little brush at the tip; not only does the tail give the jerboa support when it is standing—it also helps the animal to maintain its balance as it leaps along. It has thick hair on its feet, which absorbs some of the landing shock and serves to give a grip on shifting sand.

AN ANIMAL WE SELDOM SEE

Few people ever see a jerboa, even in localities where it is common, because this mammal stays in its den under the ground during the intense heat of the desert day; it comes out only after sunset and makes sure to retire before sunrise. Furthermore, it leaves no trace of its activities. Although the jerboa is a social animal, there are no telltale runways and, when it retires for the day, it closes up the entrance to its burrow to keep out the hot sunlight.

At night the jerboa is very fond of rolling in the cool sand and scratching itself. It will lie down on the ground, leisurely stretch out its long legs one at a time, and scratch and comb them from hip to toe with its front paws. It also uses its front paws to hold the grass seeds on which it feeds.

If you should ever meet the jerboa in its home territory, you would find it to be a medium-sized rodent, from two inches up to eight in head-and-body length. Its tail, usually about two inches longer than the head and body, is round for most of its length and broadly tufted at the tip with long black and white hairs.

The rest of the jerboa's appearance suggests its home and habits. Its ears are comparatively enormous in size—a trait we have found in other desert animals—and may equal half the length of the head and body, in some species. The eyes are large, as they often are in animals active by night. Its colour varies more or less from locality to locality, but it is usually in shades of buff mixed with black or pale russet, and the under-parts are white.

AN ANIMAL WE SELDOM SEE

The jerboa, which makes its home in the arid wastes of the Old World's deserts, is another remarkable rodent leaper. This small creature can travel by leaps and bounds considerably faster than a man can run.

SOME REMARKABLE JERBOAS

It is in Africa, Asia, and eastern Europe that we find the jerboas. The African Three-toed Jerboa, *Jaculus*, a typical member of the family, is the largest and best known of all, and has a head-and-body length of close to seven inches, and an eight-inch tail. It has been credited with a top speed of forty miles per hour, but the author has easily overtaken the animal when he travelled at that speed in a car.

Besides the typical jerboa, we find a number of others that are curiously different. There is a Fat-tailed Jerboa, a Flat-tailed Jerboa, a Dwarf Jerboa; some have five toes on the enlarged hind feet while others have only three toes. On the Big-eared Jerboa, *Euchoreutes*, of Chinese Turkistan, we see "enormous" ears measuring one and one-half inches—well, they seem enormous when you compare them with the three-inch body.

Most, if not all, jerboas sleep through the cold winter months, especially in the northern part of the range. Life begins again in April, when these animals come out of hibernation. The males are the first to appear and expend great energy in their search for a prospective mate. Very little is known about the breeding habits of these animals, but the young are born some forty-two days after mating time.

OTHER CURIOUS RATS AND MICE

There are numerous other kinds of rats, mice, and their relatives in the world, but here we have time only to glance at a few of the most curious.

Blind Rats of South-eastern Europe. The Russian peasants say that the Mediterranean Mole Rat, *Spalax*, can give you such healing skills as no medical university can teach. All you have to do is catch this furtive rodent, hold it in your bare hands, and permit it to bite you. The next and indispensable step is to squeeze it to death. For ever afterwards you will be able to cure illness simply by laying your hands on a sick person.

How such a tradition got started we can only guess, but the mole rat is without question an oddity, being one of the few mammals absolutely without sight. It has traces of eyes, but they are quite functionless and sunk below the skin. There are only vestiges of ears, and there is no tail. All in all, this robust, yellowish-brown rodent is adapted for a life under the ground, resembling the mole in habits as well as appearance. We place it in the family Spalacidae. (The name means "moles", though of course this is a different group.)

Bamboo Rats—Tastier Than Pork. Another group of burrowing rodents are the Bamboo Rats, which live in Asia and Africa. Of these, many seem to spend a good deal of their time on the surface—notably the Asiatic Bamboo Rat, *Rhizomys*, which sometimes dwells in the bamboo belt in the mountains and feeds on the roots and shoots of bamboo. Some of the bamboo rats—they make up the family Rhizo-myidae—are of a good size (well over a foot in head-and-body length); the Chinese dig them out of their dens and use them as food, preferring their flesh to pork, we are told.

Porcupines, Guinea Pigs, Chinchillas, and their Relatives

OLD WORLD PORCUPINES—
"SWORD-RATTLING WARRIORS"

THE CRESTED or Old World Porcupine, *Hystrix*, found over most of Africa, all over southern Asia, and throughout south-eastern Europe, is quite unlike its New World counterpart. So different are they, in body and habits, that we place them in separate families. Of course they both have quills, as their common name reminds us ("porcupine" originally meant "pig with spines"), but even the quills show important differences.

BIGGEST PORCUPINE ON EARTH

The crested porcupine is the largest living porcupine; it may be over three feet in length and weigh between forty and sixty pounds. Its tail is just a few inches long, quills and all.

At this point we should see why the animal is called a "crested porcupine". Extending from the nape of its neck and down its back it has a mass of quills (far longer than those in the New World species). These are real weapons—needle-pointed spines that are mixed with much longer and more slender flexible spines, or guards, measuring up to twenty-one inches in length. The guards protect the sharp points of the quills when they are not in use.

A WARNING, THEN A DEADLY BLOW

In spite of what we have often heard, the porcupine cannot shoot its quills into the flesh of an enemy. But, as already suggested, they are effective weapons none the less.

When a porcupine is disturbed, it rattles the quills on its tail. These produce a warning signal that resembles the noise created by a rattle-snake's tail.

If the sound does not make the would-be aggressor change his intentions, the "sword-rattling" warrior turns its back on him, erects its sharp rapier-like quills, and charges backwards. The bristling armament, with its multitude of sturdy spikes backed by forty pounds of porcupine, will generally damp the ardour of the most adventurous foe.

A Dead Panther. It seems, however, that many animals have more courage than sense—especially the big cats. E. C. Morris of Mysore has described how he "once came on the remains of a panther that had met its death through attacking a porcupine; the decomposed head was run through and through with no less than seventeen quills, two of which had penetrated the eyes into the brain. Its paws were also full of quills.

"The panther had evidently rushed the porcupine, which, seeing it in time, had quite obviously whirled around, presenting its back to the panther with quills erect, such being the method of defence."

GREAT DIGGERS AND HIKERS

In contrast with its tree-dwelling relatives in the New World, the crested porcupine is hardly a climber at all. It does not seem to be able to jump, either. It makes its nest in a burrow, and may live in almost any kind of country within its range, so long as it is undisturbed and there is suitable rock or brush cover. We find it in arid mountains, rocky outcrops, wooded hills, scrub-covered plains and thick forest.

The crested porcupine's nest may be one hundred feet from the entrance of the tunnel. The burrow is usually marked by the presence of well-gnawed bones and skulls strewn near the entrance (although the animal is not a killer, it likes to chew bones, much like our dogs). Often six or seven porcupines share a communal burrow or "earth", which they provide with six or seven entrances.

A seasoned hiker, the crested porcupine may travel as much as ten miles in search of food. It feeds on bulbs, the bark of trees, and fallen fruit, and is destructive to farm crops, including root tubers, pumpkins, sweet potatoes, Irish potatoes, and maize. It is commonly believed to be active only at night, but in Iran the author has seen crested porcupines about at noon and found, to his surprise, that they could gallop along a little faster than he could run.

THE BIGGEST PORCUPINE ON EARTH

The African crested porcupine, over three feet long, is the largest living porcupine. Its quills are very sharp and dangerous. When annoyed, this porcupine rattles the quills on its tail to alert the intruder, and follows the warning with a charge backwards that may mean death to the enemy. Porcupines never shoot their quills.

DANGEROUS WHEN TEN DAYS OLD

This animal mates early in the year. Its babies, numbering from one to three—but usually two—are born between six and eight weeks later, in a nest of leaves, dry grass, and root fibres. They come into the world rather well developed—their eyes are wide open and they have soft, flexible spines. The babies remain in the den until the spines have grown and hardened; these are already quite dangerous at the end of ten days.

The crested porcupine has lived for a little over twenty years in captivity, but appears to average twelve to fifteen years in the wild. With its relatives, it forms the family Hystricidae. All the animals you will read about in this chapter are called "hystricomorphs", or "porcupine shaped", and make up a rodent suborder (Hystricomorpha), named in honour of the crested porcupine. Like it, most are fairly large, and many have spines.

OTHER CURIOUS OLD WORLD PORCUPINES

Asia and Africa have some other queer-looking porcupines. The Brush-tailed Porcupine, *Atherurus*, of southern Asia and Africa, is only twenty inches in length, not including the nine-inch tail. It is a forest dweller. The long, spiny tail terminates in a tuft of stiff bristles, for which the animal is named. The odd thing about this brush is that the bristles are composed of alternating thick and thin regions, giving a fantastic appearance suggestive of a string of beads.

The Long-tailed Porcupine, *Trichys*, of the Malay Archipelago, is a smaller and comparatively soft-spined species. The South Asiatic Porcupine, *Acanthion*, is much like the familiar crested porcupine but can be recognized by the absence of the very long, slender crest quills.

NEW WORLD TREE PORCUPINES

The North American Tree Porcupine, *Erethizon*, may not be bright or fleet of foot, but it is a formidable opponent all the same. It wears a coat of some thirty thousand spines loosely attached to its skin. True, they are small and insignificant—they average about one and one-half inches each—as compared with the long, rapier-like quills of the large African and Asiatic porcupines, but they are equally effective if not more so. In reality, they are barbed darts.

30,000 QUILLS—AND HOW THEY CAN KILL

Unaggressive, good-natured creatures though they are, few porcupines meet a violent death, thanks to the protection afforded by their quills. Normally the great mass of the spines lies smoothly back as the animal ambles slowly along. Overtaken by a dangerous foe, it assumes an "on-guard" position. Its back arched, and every spine bristling, the porcupine whirls about rapidly so that it is always presenting its rear to the foe.

THE CANADIAN PORCUPINE CRAVES SALT

This quill-covered animal has a remarkable liking for salt and, prowling around cabins in the North Woods, will gnaw almost any object with human perspiration on it because of the salty taste. Porcupines prefer not to fight, even though their quills are an excellent weapon, and will attempt to escape up a tree.

If the enemy is persistent, the porcupine backs up to him. Then it will suddenly lash out with its short, well-armed club tail and drive a dozen or more quills deep into the flesh of the intruder. It strikes with lightning speed, perfect timing, and great accuracy, generally aiming for the face.

What the Quills Look Like. If you examine the quills of a porcupine closely, you will find they are slender shafts tapered at both ends with a highly polished horny surface. One end of the quill is blunt and loosely attached to muscles just under the skin. The business end of the shaft, however, is exceedingly sharp; about a thirty-second of an inch below the tip, microscopic barbs appear which increase in number back to the shoulder of the shaft. These barbs lie flat against the quill until they find their mark, usually the mouth, nose or paw of an aggressor.

"Bomb" With an Automatic Time Fuse. Each quill on the American porcupine is virtually a bomb with an automatic time fuse that explodes a few seconds after it enters the victim. The explosion is minute, but it raises the microscopic barbs on the tip of the quill. The quill cannot now be removed without literally tearing out flesh with it.

A quill can and does automatically work its way into the victim. Mountain lions, foxes, lynxes, and eagles have been killed by porcupine quills.

Pills and Quills. Canada porcupine quills are used by the American Indians, who weave them into their buckskin clothing in a decorative pattern. The author has a pair of moccasins with a handsome design of quills made by Indians on the Liard River, North-west Territories.

The Indians there told him that a number of years ago a trader sold them pink cure-all pills; but, instead of taking the pills, they dissolved them in water and used them to dye some quills, which became a most attractive shade of purple. There is now quite a demand for this particular brand of doctor's pills in the area.

THE SHUFFLING PORCUPINE

The North American tree porcupine can walk, swim, and climb, but, no matter how much it tries to hurry, the fastest gait it can achieve is a clumsy shuffle. Its home is a hole in the ground or in a hollow tree. It feeds on green vegetation most of the summer and is very fond of clover and alfalfa.

This animal does not hibernate in winter. At this time its diet is completely changed to bark, which it peels from the upper branches of evergreen trees. It sometimes causes a certain degree of damage in forested areas in this way.

Still, some written laws and certainly the unwritten law of the wilderness have put the porcupine on the protected list. You just don't shoot a porcupine. It is a quaint animal, not a very troublesome one, and moreover a man lost in the woods and starving can readily catch and kill it with a club, which cannot be said of most forest mammals. Its flesh is surprisingly tasty.

BIG PORCUPINE BABIES

Porcupines increase at a slow rate. They mate in the autumn and the young are born about seven months later. Most females have only one baby a year.

The newborn porcupine, with its eyes wide open from the very first, is fully clothed, including the spines, and is in possession of all its faculties. It weighs one pound—actually more than a newborn black bear cub—and measures a foot in length. Its nursing days are few, the Indians even claiming that the mother does not nurse her baby at all. Still, it does not reach complete maturity until the autumn of the year.

Life expectancy for the porcupine in the wild is not more than about six years. Under exceptionally ideal conditions it may live to be nine or ten years of age. Its weight averages fifteen pounds, but in some cases has reached thirty-five pounds or more.

WHERE WE FIND THEM

We find the North American tree porcupine over most of North America's forests north of the 40th parallel, and south in the Rocky Mountains to the Mexican border. The animal's entire body—limbs, head, tail, and sides of feet—is covered with thick blackish hair, which in winter completely conceals the spines. The claws are strong and curved, for climbing trees. The tail is short, broad, and well armed, as we have seen.

There are two species of North American porcupines, both large, measuring up to three feet. The Eastern Porcupine is black except for the white band on the quills, while the Western Porcupine, generally a little larger than its cousin, has greenish yellow instead of black hairs on the head.

South of the Mexican border we meet the Prehensile-tailed Porcupine, *Coendou*. Like so many other South American animals, this creature has a long tail with a naked tip, which it uses as a fifth hand to grasp hold of branches with. In fact the creature is quite capable of hanging by its tail. It is more streamlined than its North American cousins and, while it has similar spines, they are shorter and closer together.

PORCUPINE WITH A CURLING TAIL

The prehensile-tailed porcupine, at home in Latin America, can use its tail to get a firm grip on boughs and twigs as it climbs about in the trees. Its quills, though barbed and dangerous, are not nearly so long as those of its relatives to the north.

There are two other South American porcupines. One is the Short tailed Porcupine, *Echinoprocta*, of Colombia—it possesses a short, hairy, non-prehensile tail and the spines are long and only bristly on the back. The other variation on the porcupine theme dwells in Brazil: the Thin-spined Porcupine, *Chaetomys*, is covered with very wavy, bristly hairs, with sharp quills restricted to the head. We place all the New World porcupines in the family Erethizontidae—the name, appropriately enough, comes from a Greek word meaning "to irritate".

GUINEA PIGS, CAVIES, AND CUYS

The Typical Guinea Pig, Restless Cavy, or Cuy, *Cavia,* is not a pig at all, though it may grunt like one when it feels the pangs of hunger. Actually, it is a rodent of South America. Originally brought to Europe by Dutch and English slave-traders, some of whom found it in Guiana, it soon became known by its present common name.

That name, of course, is nowadays synonymous with someone or something used in an experiment. Hundreds of years ago, the Incas of Peru domesticated the wild guinea pig and used it for food, but in the United States and Europe the animal is much more familiar for the services it renders in laboratories. Because it breeds rapidly, it is used in the study of heredity, but it is also valuable for the isolation and breeding of bacteria as well as the production of serums.

— WILD AND TAME GUINEA PIGS. There is an old story that if you pick up a guinea pig by its tail, its eyes will drop out. Unfortunately, we cannot test the truth of this for ourselves, since the guinea pig has no tail. The animal is a small one—it may grow up to a foot in length—and has a rather fat body and short limbs. Its ears are short and round. Like other cavies, of which group it is typical, it lives in burrows in the ground, and favours broken brush country rather than open plains or forests. Vegetation is what it likes to eat.

The guinea pig is a fertile rodent. Although the female has only two teats, she will bear two or three young or more in a litter, twice a year in the wild. When she is domesticated, the number goes up: three or four babies are the average, and the litters come five or six times a year.

Each family is born about two months after mating time; the babies are well-developed, active little creatures, and are out feeding themselves when just a day old. At two months of age they are ready to take their turn on the guinea-pig production line. The life span is eight years, on the whole.

Guinea pigs are easily reared. They require about the same kind of accommodation as rabbits, and can be fed on the same diet. Although they are much less subject to disease than rabbits, they cannot adjust themselves so well to changes in temperature. A sudden drop downward, particularly to freezing, may prove quite injurious to them.

The guinea pig makes a friendly pet. Perhaps the most objectionable feature about it is its unpleasant odour. There is a popular belief that rats will not enter a guinea pig pen, but experience shows this to be untrue.

The rats will not only come in; they will devour their fellow rodents' food and their babies as well.

——GUINEA PIGS AS FOOD. While guinea pigs are seldom eaten in the United States, all wild cavies as well as domesticated forms are accounted good food in South America. The Moco, *Kerodon*, and especially the Rock Cuy, *Galea*, are much hunted in parts of Brazil. The Peruvian method of dressing a guinea pig for the table is much like that used for a sucking pig. The rodent is scalded in hot water, the hair is removed, and the skin is scraped with a knife. The animal is then cleaned and roasted.

These interesting little creatures are of different colours and have various kinds of fur. In some the fur is rather long and stiff, in others it is soft. The fur is reddish or greyish brown in the wild state. The majority of domestic animals are spotted; the common colours are fawn, light grey, reddish-brown, white, or black. We find the animals from Peru, Bolivia, and Argentina, to Brazil, the Guianas, Venezuela, and Colombia.

The Patagonian Cavy. Of all the strange and curious animals of South America the Patagonian Cavy, *Dolichotis*, known locally as the Mara, is one of the most amazing. It is almost harelike in appearance, with big eyes, large ears, and long legs, but the hind feet are armed with sharp, hooflike claws. The Greater Patagonian Cavy, the larger of the two species, stands about one foot at the shoulder and may attain a length of three feet.

A sociable creature, the big Patagonian cavy loves company. A dozen or more may live together in holes in the ground or bask or feed in the sun. At the first sign of danger they make off at a high speed, with a most peculiar galloping, hopping run, pausing every hundred yards or so to turn around and satisfy their curiosity. Natives hunt the big cavy for food but it is much too fast to be caught by any of the native dogs.

A FAST RUNNER

The Patagonian cavy is a long-limbed creature, and can run with great speed when pursued, as it often is, by the South American natives, who esteem it as food (it tastes much like rabbit). Like the rabbit, this odd animal has an underground retreat.

CAPYBARAS—GIANTS OF THE RODENT WORLD

The Capybara, *Hydrochoerus*, is hardly known outside its native continent of South America, yet it is the largest rodent on earth. A full-grown male capybara may stand twenty-one inches at the shoulder and measure as much as four feet in length; he may weigh over one hundred pounds.

You need not let the thought of such a great relative of the rat dismay you—the capybara looks much more like a giant edition of its closer kinsman the guinea pig. Indeed, one of its names is the Giant

Water Guinea Pig; others are Chigwire, Warpincho, and Water Hog (an accurate translation of the animal's scientific name).

It you should some day come face to face with a capybara in eastern South America, where it lives, you may safely assume there will be water near by. The animal is at home among the tall grasses that grow along the banks of such rivers as the Orinoco, and we find it as far north as Panama. Grass and water plants are the favourite foods of this inoffensive, peace-loving creature. Having eaten its fill, it likes to lie quietly and bask in the sunshine on a river bank. When pleased, it often produces a low, clicking sound.

BIG BUT PEACEABLE

The capybara, which may grow as large as a pig, is a very able swimmer. It lives along the banks of South America's mighty rivers, and is a harmless vegetarian, feeding on weeds, grass, and other plants.

——THE CAPYBARA'S ENEMIES. The shy capybara would rather run than fight. It must always be on the alert for its deadly enemies, the jaguar and the cougar. At the slightest sign of one of these, the capybara leaps to safety in the water. Though the three toes on its hind feet are only poorly webbed, it is a first-rate swimmer. It can travel long distances below the surface, too. But even in the water it dare not let down its guard, for the stream may be alligator-infested.

In a zoo, you will find that the capybara, giant of the rodent world, is a friendly animal, not so likely to flee as it is in the wild.

[3-15]

The shortest quilled and longest tailed member of the porcupine family is a tree dwelling native of South America. Like many other of its homeland's varieties of mammal, its tail is prehensile. See *page 358*

[3-15A]

The crested porcupine of Africa, southern Asia and south-eastern Europe has quills mixed with more flexible protective spines measuring up to 21 inches in length. Weighing between 40 and 60 pounds, this "pig with spines" is not a climber. See *page 351*

[3-16]

The North American porcupine with its 30,000 expanding barb quills is the most formidably armed of all. Unaggressive and good natured, the animal prefers to be let alone to pursue its clumsy shuffling way through the clover and alfalfa fields in summer and the tops of the evergeren trees in winter. *See page 354*

Animals in the Wild

ADVENTUROUS YOUNGSTERS are thrilled at the thought of stalking wild animals. It may suggest to them mighty gorillas hidden in trackless jungles or lions prowling over African plains—or perhaps a man-eating tiger that is terrorizing a village in India. They may think of the North American deer and bears, or even the smaller foxes and wildcats.

Though the animals that occur to them may be of many different kinds, one thing is certain: each will be four-legged and have fur or hair. For most children—and many parents as well!—only this type of beast is an "animal".

True, these beasts *are* animals, but they are only one type: the mammals.

Apart from mammals, we find in the animal world many creatures without four legs and fur. Among them are birds, fish, snakes, frogs, spiders, and worms. In fact, all living things that have feeling and the power of voluntary motion may properly be termed animals.

"What is the difference, then," the inquiring young mind wonders, "between mammals and other kinds of animals?"

To be considered a mammal, an animal must have three qualities. It must be warm-blooded, which means that its blood remains at nearly the same temperature no matter how hot or cold its surroundings may be. It must have hair or fur on its body. And a baby mammal is always nourished by milk furnished by its mother.

Opportunities to observe wild mammal life at first hand are much less common than those for bird study. At an early age children become familiar, to be sure, with a variety of beasts in their story books—the bears in "Goldilocks", the wolf in "Red Riding Hood", the fox in "Chicken Little"—but this acquaintance is based on fantasy rather than facts. When the youngster begins to grow away from his make-believe world and shows an interest in animals as they really are, he has considerable misinformation to discard as well as facts to learn.

Many Kinds of Mammals

A useful way to simplify the story of the mammals for an older child is to group these animals into their main divisions.

One group consists of flesh-eating ("carnivorous") mammals, such as wolves, foxes, lions, and tigers. A second group is made up of rodents—mice, squirrels, beavers and others with long, sharp front teeth. The third group, the hoofed animals, includes deer and cattle.

Strange water mammals known as manatees and dugongs are in a class by themselves—so are the flying mammals we call bats. Whales are probably the best known of the group known as "cetaceans".

THE FIERCE AND CRUEL TIGER
We picture the great cat as a prowler of the Indian jungle, though tigers of some kinds are found in cooler regions of Asia. The tiger hunts wild animals, though it will sometimes seize village livestock or even human beings.

All toothless mammals such as the ant-eater are included in one group. Finally there are the marsupials, made up chiefly of mammals with pouches in which to carry their babies. The kangaroo of Australia is perhaps the most widely known of the pouched animals.

Flesh Eaters and Plant Eaters

On the basis of their food habits mammals may be divided into two general classes. There are plant eaters (herbivores) and flesh eaters (carnivores). In trying to distinguish one type from the other, a child would pretty much take for granted that the flesh eaters are larger and stronger. But that is not always the case. Teeth and claws are a better basis for distinguishing between the two groups. You can point out that the flesh eater has sharp enlarged canine teeth, shearing side teeth, and strong, sharp claws.

Hunting for Animal Tracks

When your child becomes interested in the activities of wild mammals, you can join him in a fascinating hobby: hunting for footprints and identifying them. You may start track-hunting by going to likely places such as muddy stream banks and finding tracks there, identifying them later—or you may first obtain a background for field study from books and observations near home. In your own back yard you may find the tracks of dogs, cats, and squirrels.

A dog's tracks are easily distinguished from a cat's, for while a dog's claws make tiny marks in front of its toeprints, a cat's claws do not touch the ground during normal walking or running. All members of the cat family (except only the cheetah) are able to pull their claws back into protective sheaths when they are not using them. Pussy always walks on "velvet paws"!

It is more difficult to tell a dog's track from a fox's, though the marks of a fox's toes and the ball of its foot are very nearly circular, whereas those of a dog are often long-shaped or triangular. The ball of a dog's foot also leaves a deeper mark than that of a fox. But if there is a whole set of footprints the question is easily settled. A fox always steps into its own footmarks and so leaves a single straight line of equally-spaced

LANGUAGE A TRACKER CAN READ

Left are the tracks of a house cat. Next come the tracks of a dog—note the claw marks.
Second from right are the footprints of the fox. The tracks on the right say that "Brock
the Badger passed this way!"

depressions, but a dog's feet come down in separate places and leave a
zig-zag line of double marks.

Tracks in the Snow. Tracks are generally to be seen only in soft
ground, whether sandy or muddy, and suitable patches may be hard to

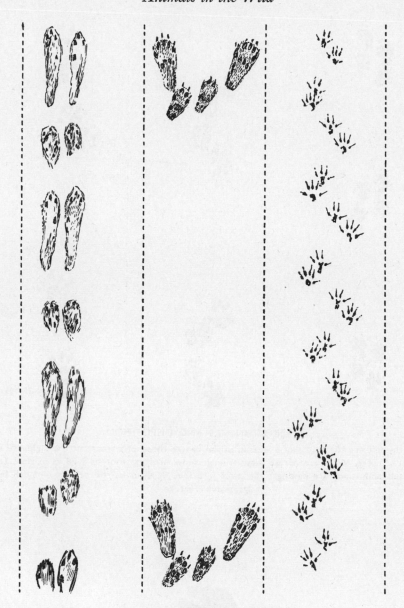

MORE CONTRASTS IN FOOTMARKS

On the left, the tracks of a rabbit. Centre, those of the grey squirrel. The light, spread-out tracks on the right are those of the field mouse, which places its hind feet partly in the tracks left by its fore feet.

find. However, the first fall of snow in winter may provide a wealth of examples, especially if you leave food-scraps outside your garden door at night. You may easily recognize dog and cat tracks in thin snow,

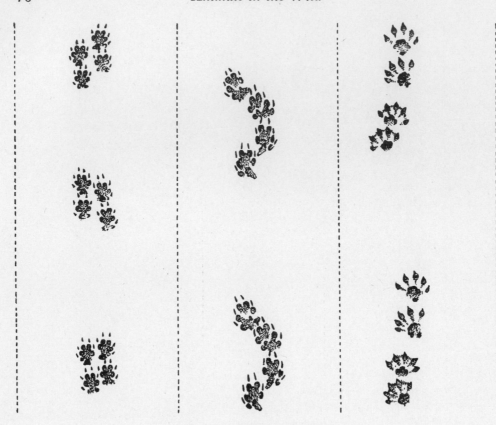

DIFFERENT IN SIZE AND DISPOSITION

On the left are the tracks of a weasel, in the centre those of a stoat. At the right are an otter's tracks. What a contrast these animals show in disposition as well as in size! The weasels and stoats are amongst the most ferocious of animals; the otter is a much less aggressive creature.

TRACKS OF THE RED DEER

Here are tracks of a very different kind—those of a larger and heavier animal. The red deer's hoofprints are called "slots". The cloven hoof enables the deer to travel swiftly and surely over yielding ground and across rough country.

and the "star-like" marks of birds' feet, but among them there may also be the tracks of rats, voles, shrews and field mice. These animals do not hibernate and must therefore forage for food.

The track of the long-tailed field mouse is especially interesting, for it places its hind feet partly in the marks made by its fore feet, thus lengthening them, and between the two rows of tracks there is a line showing where it dragged its tail along. The tip of the tail is raised and swung sideways every three or four steps, first to one side and then to the other, thus breaking the line.

How Mammals Talk

You will probably be surprised at the number of animal sounds you can hear if you are very quiet yourself and keep quite still. Of course, you must be in a field or by a ditch where there are animals to be heard, and the best time is generally fairly early in the morning or late in the evening. So many animals sleep by day and come out only at night that you have to catch them in the dusk when they are either going back to bed or just thinking of coming out.

In the early morning you may see rabbits feeding, but though rabbits are usually silent animals they often utter a brief "huck!" two or three times when they are pleased about something. But the small animals most commonly heard are the little field mice and the shrews.

The long-tailed field mouse is a very pretty little creature which lives in a hole in the ground. When it comes out to forage for dainty food—such as the bulbs of the best garden flowers!—it often stands on its hind legs and washes itself, making a comfortable chuckling sound. It may do this only a few yards away from you, for it is very short-sighted, and unless you move or are on the windward side of it, it probably has no idea that you are there.

THE QUARRELSOME SHREW

The common shrew, which is about by day as well as by night, is a voracious eater and will die if not fed every few hours. It can eat three times its own weight in a day and is always squabbling and fighting over its food. It can frequently be heard shrieking and squealing, even when it cannot be seen, but the sound is not very loud to human ears, and is so high-pitched that some people cannot hear it at all.

Another animal you may hear in the daytime is the hedgehog, which sleeps in a ditch or buried in leaves and brushwood and snores loudly. You can hear its snores from a distance of several yards, and your first thought is generally that a tramp must be asleep under the hedge! To hear its voice you must go out at night, but this is hardly profitable, since the hedgehog is usually a silent animal. It sometimes grunts, but is said to squeal if attacked by a badger. The young hedgehogs squeak.

In the daytime, too, you may hear the red squirrel barking, but this animal also has a great variety of lesser cries. When frightened it makes a long string of querulous noises. This is our native squirrel. The more common grey squirrel, which is an immigrant from America, is more silent. However, it scolds and complains by making a kind of growl which has been spelt as "chur-r-r!"

How Animals Fight

Very few animals enjoy fighting except at mating time, when it is common for the males to fight for possession of a female. Of course, the flesh-eaters have to attack and kill their prey, and this involves a fight to the death, but it is unusual for the contest to be equal. The hunter selects prey which he knows he can kill easily, and the affair is a job of work rather than a fight. Unexpected things sometimes happen, however, and a cornered animal may turn surprisingly fierce and even drive off its attacker.

But what we call "warfare", in which a group of animals attacks another group *of the same species*, is completely unknown in the animal kingdom—if we except the doubtful case of one species of ant. There is no natural "instinct" to war; war is one of the more distressing inventions of man and first appeared only a few thousands of years ago.

When animals do have occasion to fight they follow no "Queensberry Rules". Teeth and claws are the chief weapons, but many hoofed animals use their horns and some—for example, the horse—can kill with a kick. When two male deer or stags fight they use the knife-sharp hoofs of their forefeet to inflict crippling wounds on each other. They also butt with their huge, branching antlers and it sometimes happens that these become locked together. If they cannot disentangle themselves they will fall to the ground when they are exhausted, and may perish miserably of starvation.

Dressing Up for Battle. A stag that is spoiling for a fight makes curious preparations for it. It hunts about with bloodshot eyes, roaring like a

THE HANDSOME RED DEER

Though the stag is equipped with spreading antlers for attack and defence, the red deer's grace and beauty suggest watchfulness and instant, rapid movement if danger threatens. Red deer are found in many countries, but the Highlands of Scotland are specially famous for them. In the mating season, the stags fight for the hinds.

lion, until it finds a peat bog, in which it wallows. It comes out dripping with black mud and is then ready to fight any other male who dares to approach its herd of females. When in such a mood it will not hesitate to attack a human intruder, and it is always dangerous to approach a stag in the mating or "rutting" season, which is the autumn.

ANTLERS AND HORNS

The antlers of a full-grown stag may be more than thirty-three inches long and branch into twelve or more sharp tines or "points", yet they are shed every spring and a new set is grown before the autumn. They develop from two bony knobs on the skull and are themselves made of bone. While they are growing they are covered with a soft substance called "velvet", which is full of blood-vessels and protected by a fine down. The velvet is very sensitive and tender, but when the bone is fully formed it dries up and the stag rubs it off against the trunk of a tree. The stag uses its antlers chiefly to control its herd of females (which do not have antlers). The females are called "hinds" or "does" and the stags are sometimes referred to as "harts".

The horns of cattle and goats, and those of the antelopes and gazelles of warmer countries, are quite different from a deer's antlers. They are made of horn and not of bone, though the horn is hollow and fits over a bony projection on the skull. Such horns are not shed every year; once grown they are permanent. The horn of a rhinoceros is different again—it consists of a closely-packed mass of horny fibres, growing from the skin like bristles.

A young male deer has no antlers until it is three years old. The knobs on the skull first develop in the second year, when the animals are called "knobbers", and a year later tiny antlers consisting of one point each appear. Each year after that the new set of antlers has one more point until the full number is reached in about twelve years. An animal with twelve points is called a "stag royal".

The Largest British Animals

The red deer is the largest British wild animal, and it is found chiefly in the north of Scotland, though a few live on Exmoor, in Devonshire, and in the New Forest. Next in size come the wild ponies of Exmoor and the New Forest, and the smaller deer.

Of the wild ponies there are two distinct varieties, one of which is a dwarf, but the word "pony" has no well-defined meaning apart from "small horse". Though many of the ponies have lived a wild or semi-wild life as long as man can remember, in many districts their breeding is more or less regulated and they are rounded up, counted and branded periodically. Many are broken in and sold.

The heaths of the New Forest are very poor in pasture and the hardy ponies of this region are said to be the only large animals able to feed on unprepared gorse, holly and woody twigs through the winter. Ponies of similar size are also found on Exmoor, Dartmoor and in parts of Wales. They are shy, nervous and unpredictable animals, so it is just as well that they are difficult to approach. They are best watched from a distance, and children should never be allowed to go among them.

HE OFTEN LIVES IN A PARK

This is the fallow deer. Many are kept in parks and large private grounds. Quick and wary, they are notable for their broad, flat antlers. In summer they are fawn with whitish spots, in winter they take on a greyish tone.

The dwarf pony is the picturesque Shetland, with its long mane and shaggy coat. It stands only three feet high and, being small and very docile, is a great favourite with children, but it is not often seen outside the Shetland Islands or in the neighbourhood of mines, where it was once used for working underground.

Intermediate in size between the two varieties of pony comes the fallow deer, and smaller even than the Shetland pony is the little roe deer. These two pretty animals are seldom seen in the wild state except in the national and larger private parks, and in the New Forest, but today the deer population in the New Forest is very small. The roe deer is native, but the spotted fallow deer was introduced by the Romans.

SPECIAL SCENT GLANDS

Deer have good sight and hearing and are very clever at concealing themselves. They may remain completely motionless so that a traveller may pass within a few yards without noticing them. But their sense of smell is so highly developed that they can scent a man up to a distance of about a mile when the wind is right. They follow their own tracks by scent, a special gland in their hind-feet leaving a trail of scent on the ground.

Another animal equipped with a scent gland is the fox, but this is situated beneath the tail. The fox scent is repulsive to most other animals and serves the purpose of deterring strangers or enemies, but it is easily followed by fox-hounds. The fox is well aware of this and is cunning enough to break its trail by taking to water, leaping over a wall, or climbing a tree and leaving it by a long low-hanging branch.

There seems to be no end to the tricks a fox will get up to to break its trail. It will sometimes retrace its path a short distance and then leap sideways to break the continuity, thus leaving a sort of *cul-de-sac* to puzzle hounds. It will mingle with a flock of sheep to confuse its scent with theirs, or even roll in evil-smelling muck to smother its own scent.

SQUIRRELS—NATURE'S ACROBATS

Of all the wild four-footed animals, the grey squirrel is probably the one most commonly observed by children. He dwells in wooded regions, and also in city parks and suburban areas as well. In fact, these attractive rodents seem to prefer the hazards of civilization to the dangers of the wilds, and their habits vary little whether they live in town or country.

Young Squirrels. Watch for young squirrels about the middle of May. A mother bears four to six infants during March, and she may have a second litter during the summer. She gives her young devoted care.

They are born blind and hairless. When they are about six weeks old they begin to climb around the tree branches and nibble at buds and leaves. At eight or nine weeks they have a full coat of fur and are about half grown.

In a year they have almost reached full growth and are able to leap among the branches with astounding agility. The bushy tail is a great help in balancing and making easy landings possible.

During cold weather squirrels generally live in a hollow tree, but later in the year they find a suitable location, usually thirty feet from the ground in the crotch of a tree, and there they construct a nest of dead leaves and sticks. The shape of the nest is a clue to the tenant's identity. A bird's nest is flattened at the top; the squirrel's is rounded. Red squirrels also build nests—sprawling but comfortable ones of bark, twigs, leaves or moss. A squirrel's nest is called a drey.

Squirrels and Food. As you watch a squirrel bury a nut in the ground, you may well ask yourself: Will he ever find it again? It would be a mistake to think that all the nuts that are buried get dug up afterward. This is especially true in the wilds where food is plentiful; and for this reason the squirrel makes a valuable contribution to replanting the forests.

Apart from nuts, squirrels enjoy the seeds from apples, pears, and other fruit, mushrooms, corn, and wheat. Sometimes they raid birds' nests for eggs or fledgelings, though they are guilty of such raids less often than red squirrels. An overabundance of peanuts is unhealthy for squirrels, but a few added to tree nuts or other foods are a nourishing addition to their diet.

Rabbits and Hares

Rabbits and hares belong to the same family and look very much alike, yet their habits are very different. For one thing, rabbits live in burrows which often run back into a bank or hill for many yards, and much of their time is spent in excavating them, but hares live entirely in the open and can scarcely be said to have a "home" at all. Rabbits are sociable animals and many families may share the same "warren", but hares are solitary creatures and you seldom see two together.

In the breeding season the female rabbit or "doe" usually digs a new breeding-hole, about two feet long, and at the bottom of it makes a nest of leaves, ferns and down plucked from her own body. The bunnies are born naked and blind, and with their ears closed. Their eyes open on the eleventh day and their ears on the twelfth. On the fourteenth they

A SPEEDY RUNNER

Hares of many kinds are found in different countries of the world. This is the European brown hare, common in Britain, where it may be seen crossing a field or open land at high speed with a loping, jumping gait.

can run about and are self-supporting in a month. They begin breeding themselves at six months and live for seven or eight years.

The March Hare. Now compare this with the life of a hare. It has no safe burrow to hide in, but finds a comfortable depression in the turf in which it crouches.

This is known as the hare's "form" and it is chosen according to the weather, sometimes benefiting from the sun or providing a good view round, and at others ensuring shelter from wind or rain.

In the courting season a male (or "buck") will run about all day looking for a female, leaping and cavorting as if he always expected the doe to be hiding behind him or lurking just beyond the next tuft of grass.

When at these antics he is known as a "March hare", and if he secures a doe he will fight off all rivals by standing on his hind-legs and "boxing".

A doe produces from two to five leverets, but this may happen at any season and not only in the spring. The mother then finds separate forms for each leveret and carries them to their solitary nurseries in her mouth. They are left alone most of the time, but she goes round periodically to suckle them, both by day and night. The leverets are born covered with hair and with both eyes and ears open. They are also able to run about, and within a month become completely independent.

CUNNING AS A FOX

A hare is a swift runner but its long hind legs put it at a disadvantage when running downhill. When it leaves or arrives at its form it will make two great sideways leaps of about fifteen feet to break its scent. When hunted, it is said to be as cunning as a fox. It will drive sheep or cattle away from its form by "boxing", the larger animals sheering off in alarm at this uncanny spectacle. The hare is a silent animal and expresses pleasure by panting—a process which raises its temperature.

THE CUNNING FOX

A vixen (left) and a dog fox look round warily for signs of danger. When he is hunted, the fox is not only speedy but full of tricks—doubling, jumping, running along walls and through brooks to throw pursuers off the scent.

Hares live on the moors where there is very little cover, so they seek concealment by crouching down with their ears flattened, when they look very much like smooth stones. There is a country saying that if you are in doubt as to whether a brown or grey object is a stone or a hare, walk towards it.

If it is a stone it will appear to get larger and larger as you approach, but if it is a hare it will get smaller and smaller!

Mice and Rats—Pets and Pests

The house mouse, originally a native of Asia, is responsible for much of the dislike visited on the whole tribe. Through its ability to stow away wherever food is kept, this creature infiltrated into Europe and has

THE LONG-TAILED FIELD MOUSE
He lives in a hole in the ground, and comes out to feed on fruit and other vegetation—including the bulbs of garden flowers! He also eats insects, dead leaves and young, helpless birds. He is suspected of being a cannibal.

made its way (by ship) to America. Although this mouse usually makes its home in houses or barns, it sometimes nests under cornstalks or in grain fields.

Indoors it uses the space between plaster and outer walls for runways, or else it travels between ceiling and floor. With its strong gnawing teeth it can easily cut through wood, cardboard, or almost any obstacle but metal. The mother mouse makes her nest out of cloth, paper, or whatever pliable material she can find.

The Harvest Mouse. This pretty creature is the second smallest British mammal, the smallest being the pygmy shrew. Unfortunately, it is becoming rare, although it is probably still far from extermination. It is so adept at escaping notice that it was not known to exist until the eighteenth century, when it was discovered by Gilbert White. It is found in the south and east of England, in part of the Midlands, and in south-east Scotland.

It lives among grasses and gets its name from its fondness for nesting in growing corn. When seen at all, it is generally during the reaping of a cornfield. It builds a ball-shaped nest of grass and leaves about the size of an orange, less than a foot from the ground. It is supported by three or four cornstalks passing through it, and is lined with chewed grass and leaves. The entrance is at the side and the mother closes it when she goes in or out. It holds up to nine babies at a time, as well as the mother, but this is no great weight, since the adult harvest mouse turns the scale at only one-sixth of an ounce!

In climbing it makes great use of its tail, which it will wind several times round a cornstalk by way of anchor while it explores an ear of corn. It does not jump, but passes from stalk to stalk by reaching sideways. It hibernates through the winter in a moss-lined nest inside a rick, or sometimes supported by reeds over water.

The Dormouse. Most peoples' acquaintance with the dormouse is limited to an illustrated passage in *Alice in Wonderland*, yet it is a fairly common animal in the Midlands and south of England, and in Wales. It is less common in the north and is not found in Scotland. It is a little smaller than the house mouse, and lives in woods, copses and hedgerows. Though seldom seen, it likes living near houses and gardens.

The dormouse gets its name from its profound winter sleep, which it takes in a nest built underground or hidden among the roots of bushes. While hibernating it becomes cold and stiff and can be handled—and even rolled about—without waking. In spring, it builds a breeding-nest of grass, moss and bark, lined with leaves. This is generally situated in a thicket a few inches above the ground.

The dormouse is a pretty and agile creature. It jumps well and when feeding sits up and uses its hands like a squirrel. Its food includes fruit, seeds and nuts, as well as insects, birds' eggs and even small birds. Its very faint squeak can hardly be heard, unless you are very close.

RATS AND VOLES

Britain has two species of rat, the brown and the black, but since the black rat (or "long-tailed rat") is now found only in a few dockyards the brown rat is the one commonly met with. Its body is usually about eight or nine inches long, and its scaly tail nearly the same length. Well-fed rats have, however, been known to grow to twelve inches, with an eleven-inch tail, which is larger than a squirrel. It lives everywhere, from hedgerow and barnyard to warehouse and city sewer. There is no such animal as a "sewer rat"—this mythical creature is a brown rat which happens to inhabit the sewers.

The black rat seldom exceeds nine inches in length, but its tail is longer than its body. It takes little pleasure in the sewers, preferring to live above ground, and is most at home on board ship. Another rodent as large as the brown rat, and even heavier, is the so-called "water-rat", but this creature is not a rat but a vole.

The voles, of which there are four British species, are more closely related to the mice than to the rats, but they can generally be distinguished from both at a glance by their short muzzles. The bank vole lives in shallow burrows dug out among the hedge-roots, and often shares them with mice, shrews and other voles. From its main burrow it drives a narrower one, too small for rats or moles to enter, and at the bottom of it makes a nest of chewed grass.

The Water Vole. The water vole, like the smaller bank vole, is common all over Britain, but it digs its burrows either in the bank of a stream or near by. The burrows lead to the water and form a complex maze with entrances both below and above the water-line. Though an excellent swimmer, the water vole does not usually eat fish or frogs, as is commonly supposed, but is almost entirely a vegetarian. It eats all day and does not hibernate, though it stays at home in severe winter weather and feeds on a store of food collected in the autumn.

It is a water-loving animal, yet it is not such a strong swimmer as the

AMONGST THE REEDS AND RUSHES
The water vole is a common sight on British rivers. When alarmed he dashes off, and can move faster under water than he can swim on the surface.

brown rat (which is not particularly fond of water). When alarmed, a water vole dives into the stream or pond with a loud "plop!" and this is often the only evidence of its presence. It would do better to stay still! However, it seldom remains under water as long as half a minute, when it can be seen swimming off some distance away from the circle of ripples caused by its dive.

Otters—Shy but Likeable

A much larger water-mammal is the otter, which may be thirty inches in length and have a fur-covered tail which adds another twenty inches. Though by no means uncommon on all the larger rivers of Britain, otters are seldom seen except when hunted because they come abroad only at night or in the dusk. They also live on various deserted stretches of the coast, where they may be called "sea-otters". They live in holes which are more like deep caves than burrows, and keep a separate chamber as an earth-closet.

An otter's lair is called a "holt", and it is often made under the roots of a tree growing at the water's edge. The main entrance is under water, but there is usually a dry "bolt-hole" on the land as well. The young, called "whelps", are born blind and remain so for five weeks, but the mother carries them under the water even before they can see.

THEY LIVE NEAR RIVERS AND LAKES
The otter in Britain. Otters of various kinds live near rivers and lakes in many countries.
The sea otter is found along the shores of the North Pacific.

Otters Outswim Fish. Otters are remarkably swift and agile in the water: they catch the fish they delight to eat, literally out-swimming them! Yet young otters are anything but "born swimmers". They live quietly at first, feeding on their mother's milk. After about eight weeks she takes them for their first swimming lesson. By way of encouraging a baby she has it climb on her shoulders; then she dives into the water, often swimming with the baby still clinging to her. Lessons may continue throughout the summer until the young otters are as big as cats. Painstaking practice finally turns the pupils into first-class swimmers.

The Otters' Playful Habits. An otter family keeps together for at least a year, and all its members, parents as well as youngsters, know how to have fun the way boys and girls do. A pastime the otters favour, for example, is for two of them to pull at opposite ends of a stick, tug-of-war fashion. They romp and roll like puppies, clawing up the turf and throwing the clods about. Their greatest fun comes from sliding. They love to chute-the-chute on their stomachs down steep river banks into the water, and will keep this up in one place until it becomes very slippery. In wintertime they toboggan down snow-covered hills.

GAMBOLS ON THE SHORE

The sea-otters are just as playful on the shore, and in many such places —though not in the populated south-east—seals may often be seen. The British Isles have two species of seal. The grey seal is common in the Outer Hebrides, the west coast of Ireland and the Scilly Isles, but it has also been found on the east coast of England as far south as the Wash. The common seal may be found almost anywhere, except near the towns, and sometimes it even comes into the mouth of the Thames as far as Tilbury.

The grey seal is the larger, but otherwise they both look much alike, the males being darker on the back. Both are pale underneath and covered all over with spots like a Dalmatian dog, but the grey seal is sometimes very nearly black all over. They live in flocks of as many as a hundred (or more) and frequent small islets and other such places where shelter may be found. They remain on and about the same rocks for long periods, polishing them smooth, but at the breeding season the females form a separate herd until the young are born.

THE ISLANDS OF THE SIRENS

The common seal is a friendly creature and can easily be tamed unless it has had unfortunate experiences with fishermen or hunters. While active it can swim under water for five minutes or more without taking breath, but it sleeps under water and then comes up automatically for breath every quarter of an hour or so.

The voice of the seal suggests a child or a woman singing a call which sounds like "Who-ee!" It is heard often at night and is sometimes very melodious. It has been suggested that the singing of seals gave rise to the ancient myth of the islands of the Sirens, but if so Ulysses must have been content with a very limited repertoire! In the daytime seals often come ashore to bask in the sun, but they do not move easily over land. They can lumber along at three miles per hour, as against their swimming speed of ten or twelve miles per hour.

MOLES—NATURE'S EXCAVATORS

You do not have to go far afield for evidence of moles. All too often unsightly ridges appear in your garden or lawn which proclaim that these strange, near-blind underground mammals have been tunnelling there. But though they live near human dwellings, moles are seldom seen. This endows them with a rather mysterious quality for a child, who quite naturally wonders how an animal can dig up the ground while it is actually under it.

A WONDERFUL TUNNELLER

The familiar molehill only hints at a wonderful system of underground tunnels. Powerful forelegs and sharp claws enable the mole to cut through the earth at incredible speed.

The mole itself is a very interesting creature, though it is seldom seen except dead in a mole-trap. The writer, however, once surprised a mole on his lawn in broad daylight. The mole was probably the quicker to "spy strangers" and at once began digging into the soft turf. It seemed to disappear by magic and was certainly out of sight in half a minute.

This mole had probably come up for worms driven to the surface by recent rains. A mole will actually jump out of the ground after a worm. It may eat as many as sixty worms a day and is very particular how it does so. It first bites off the tail, then turns the worm round and eats it from the head end, gradually squeezing all the earth out of the worm's severed tail. Moles also eat insects and their grubs, and occasionally catch lizards, frogs, mice, shrews and young birds.

Moles swim very well and for long distances, and their normal mode of progression through their earth tunnels is a sort of "rowing", for their forefeet are turned outwards like the blades of a pair of oars. With these they can lever themselves along at a great rate, their hind legs pushing as the "oars" are brought forward for the next pull. So that it can move backwards or forwards with equal ease, a mole's fur is short and stands straight out from the skin like the "pile" of velvet. It is possibly the only animal whose hair does not lie down one way or the other. Its fur is, indeed, very much like soft velvet, and was once in great demand for making waistcoats.

How the Mole Burrows. When the mole is digging, it braces itself with one of its short powerful front paws while the other pushes the soil upward—this is how the ridges that disfigure your lawn are created. To make deeper tunnels, the mole scoops the earth under its body and pushes it as far back as possible with its back feet. Every now and then the mole turns a somersault and then proceeds in the opposite direction, shoving the accumulated pile of dirt along until it comes to a vertical tunnel excavated on a previous occasion. Here the mole forces the dirt up into the open, forming the proverbial "molehill".

The mole's nest, lined with grass and leaves, is some six to twelve inches below the surface of the ground. A main passageway leads from the nest to a series of tunnels extending in all directions. Most of these tunnels lead in turn to hunting grounds where worms and grubs abound, but one tunnel is reserved for an exit when danger threatens.

"Mr. Prickles" Comes for Milk

Another animal which may be seen in the garden, especially late in the dusk, is the hedgehog. If you have reason to believe your garden is being visited by a hedgehog, you may encourage it to show itself by leaving a saucer of milk, or bread-and-milk, near your garden door. If the milk disappears in the night it may, of course, have been taken by a cat or any other animal, but if the culprit is a hedgehog it will presently

PROTECTED BY HIS SPINES

Other animals sometimes think that the hedgehog would make a tasty meal, but when he rolls into a spiky ball the attacker may have second thoughts. Hedgehogs prowl by night, though they are sometimes seen by day. They eat insects of many kinds, as well as snails, worms, frogs, rats, mice, eggs and even snakes.

come within sight at dusk and sit down to wait for the milk to be put out. After a time it will come at the rattle of the saucer and regard you with a friendly eye while it sups.

The "prickles" or spines of a hedgehog serve several purposes, protection from dogs and other animals being only one. If alarmed it will roll up in a ball and present sharp spines in every direction, so that a dog which sniffs at it receives only a painful prick in the nose. The fox and the badger, and a few dogs, know how to unroll a hedgehog and kill it, but the male hedgehog or "boar" will fight fiercely for its life.

Another use for the prickles is in locomotion. If alarmed near a bank or ditch the hedgehog will scuttle to the edge and curl into a ball, and will then roll swiftly down the slope and out of sight. The prickles also serve as "buffers" when it reaches the bottom or if it strikes a stone. In the late autumn, preparation for hibernation often includes a roll in the dead leaves, which stick on the spines and provide a coat as well as camouflage.

Though slow-moving as a rule, a hedgehog can run quite quickly, and is a good swimmer. It catches and eats insects, slugs, worms, frogs, rats, mice and birds. It is also partial to snakes, catching an adder by first biting its tail and then rolling up quickly, when the adder strikes and kills itself on the hedgehog's spines.

Wild Pets

A hedgehog which will come to be fed at the backdoor is what we mean by a "wild pet". Wild animals should never be shut up in hutches or cages, but it is possible to make friends with many without attempting to "catch" them. It must always be cruel to shut up a wild animal, but there is another reason for not making too close an acquaintance with the hedgehog. This animal is often crawling with vermin, and though its parasites would not take to a human body they are unpleasant "extras"!

Squirrels, too, may be encouraged to come for nuts and fruit, and Frances Pitt, the naturalist, once made friends with a polecat. But with nervous creatures like these it is of no use going out to them with a handful of food, calling "Pretty pussy!" They will not come on those terms. The best procedure is to sit or picnic near a spot where they have been seen, and to keep quite still—perhaps reading a book—for an hour or two at a time. Be careful to make no sudden movements or extravagant gestures, and often close the eyes as if going to sleep.

If you have left food scraps lying about at a little distance from you the animals will, sooner or later, come and take them, but before this happens in your presence you may have to sit through many picnics, always at the same place and at the same time of day. When they show no signs of fear you may pointedly offer them food, but never throw it at them. Toss it with a minimum of movement in a direction slightly away from them. If you persevere they may eventually come and take scraps from your hand, but they dislike being thrown at. If you are lucky enough to be able to do this sitting in your own back garden, you may eventually find a squirrel following you indoors!

"Brock" the Badger

A large animal much more common than is generally realized is the badger. Even today, badgers are known to live within ten miles of London, and they are found in nearly every county throughout the British Isles. They are said to be getting scarcer (which is hardly surprising) but the chief reason they are not seen more often is that they are strictly nocturnal animals and are extremely adept at concealing their presence.

The male and female badger are called the "boar" and "sow" respectively, and the boar, which is slightly the larger, may measure twenty-eight inches from snout to rump, with a small eight-inch tail on the end. The badger is known at a glance by its long snout and the black and white stripes along its head and face. It eats everything, from roots and fruit to slugs, wasps' nests, moles, snakes and rabbits.

The badger lives in a deep burrow called a "set" (often wrongly spelt "sett", or even "sette"). A set may run ten feet down into the ground and have more than one chamber at the bottom. There may also be several passages and more than one opening. To achieve these feats of digging the badger selects sandy soil and usually leaves a huge pile of excavated earth outside the main entrance. When this has grassed over it serves to hide the opening.

In one of the chambers the badger makes its bed of leaf-mould, grass and fern-fronds. Every spring it drags its bedding out to dry in the sun and prepares new chambers and bedding in preparation for breeding. The badger is a very clean animal, burying its dung in an earth-hole a long way from its set. It carefully cleans its claws on a tree-trunk before going indoors. The sow is as particular as a cat in keeping its young—called "earth-pigs"—clean, but it is said to litter only once in three years. The cubs are born six at a time and do not come out of the set for two months.

The badger is a sociable animal, several families sometimes living together in a warren of sets connected together below ground. A warren with as many as forty entrances has been found. When abroad, the

A CREATURE OF THE NIGHT

During the day the shy badger likes to stay at home in his "earth" which is reached by the long tunnels of his "set". He makes a bed of leaves, moss and straw. He eats insects, small animals, fruit, nuts and vegetables.

badger moves with a rolling shuffle, rather like a bear, and is every bit as cunning as a fox. It is even said to have perfected a method of snapping a gin trap by rolling on it, and then making off with the bait.

LODGING TO LET

Foxes often make use of abandoned badger sets, for they hardly ever dig their own holes. A fox's hole is properly called an "earth", but a fox prefers to find a vacant burrow to doing any excavating itself, though it generally takes the trouble to stop up every entrance except the least noticeable one. However, space in its adopted home need not necessarily be vacant, so long as there is plenty of room for a lodger, and badgers and foxes not infrequently live together.

Most foxes' earths are old rabbit burrows, perhaps slightly enlarged for comfort, and it is not unknown for a fox to be living in one part of a warren while the bunnies continue to live in another part. The two families may become quite friendly and play together, the fox going out to do its hunting elsewhere. However, if food is scarce it is handy to be able to eat your neighbours—the rabbits cannot count, and do not seem to miss an occasional bunny!

Stoats and Weasels

Stoats and weasels are small animals very much alike in general appearance and closely related, but they are easily distinguished if you know what to look for. A full-grown stoat is about ten inches long, plus a five-inch tail, the tail being about half as long as the head and body. A weasel is not only smaller, its head and body measuring about eight inches, but its two-inch tail is only a quarter as long as its head and body. This difference in tail-length is very noticeable when the animals are running, for the stoat's tail is long enough to wave up and down, while the weasel's remains straight.

Both animals have short legs, and their small heads, long necks and slender bodies give them a snakelike appearance. When a stoat is running, waves of motion pass from its head to its tail so that it looks very much like a snake. A weasel glides along more smoothly. There is no mistaking their curious motions, even when seen in a bad light or just "out of the corner of your eye". A direct look shows another difference. Though both animals are chestnut brown with light under-parts, the tip of the stoat's tail is black.

The under-side of a weasel's body is white and always looks beautifully clean. That of the stoat is cream-coloured except in severe winters, when the whole animal (except for the tip of the tail) turns white and is called an "ermine". Weasels do not turn white in the winter in Britain, and even stoats rarely make a complete change, especially in the south.

INTREPID HUNTERS

Both stoats and weasels make nests in hollow trees, in a hole in a wall and other such places. They are frequently about during the daytime hunting rats, mice, rabbits and other small creatures. They readily attack animals larger than themselves, but in ratting a weasel is more courageous than a stoat. A weasel will scratch out a tunnel in a rick and make its way to the top, where it will suddenly pounce out and capture sparrows.

The writer once let a six-months-old kitten out of his back door for a short run in the dusk, and was horrified to see from an upstairs window that it was standing still in the middle of the lawn watching a stoat running round it in circles. The kitten seemed disposed to play, but hardly knew what to make of its strange visitor. By the time the writer reached the garden the kitten was dead, killed by an almost invisible bite through the arteries of its neck.

The stoat performs its dance to mesmerize its victims and always kills by this method. It does not suck the blood, as is often supposed, but drags its victim off to its nest and eats it there. By pulling and pushing it is said to be able to take off a carcass of four times its own weight, but in the case of the kitten the stoat had been scared away by the writer's quick arrival on the scene. Hares and rabbits become paralysed at the appearance of a stoat, and await their death motionless but screaming.

Both stoats and weasels perform great service to farmers by keeping down rats and other vermin, but as they also steal eggs they are enemies of the gamekeeper. They will take eggs from partridges' or pheasants' nests (which are on the ground) by rolling them away, using their chins and pushing with their breasts.

A HAPPY FAMILY

One evening the writer was sitting in his garden when he noticed with astonishment what appeared to be a model railway train with six coaches travelling smoothly along a bank about fifty yards away. The light was not very good, but fortunately the train came round in a curve and crossed a corner of the lawn, keeping in perfect alignment as if running on rails.

He then saw that this was a weasel taking its family out—perhaps to teach the cubs to hunt! It was a really beautiful procession, the chestnut and white being spotless, and each cub kept its nose to the tail of the one in front so that the chain was never broken. Suddenly the mother (presumably) took alarm and wheeled sharply to the right, and in a flash the train had vanished through a gap in a hedge.

This head-to-tail formation is probably one of the uses weasels make of a scent gland by their tails, though the scent is repulsive to humans and most other animals. It is generally supposed to be used to keep enemies at a distance, and the stoat certainly emits a similar stench to check pursuers.

Ferret and Polecat

The stoat, weasel, ferret and polecat are all members of the same genus, the ferret being probably an albino variety of Asiatic polecat. It is not a wild animal in Britain, but has been bred for use in catching rabbits and rats since Roman times. The male ferret is called a "hob" and the female a "jill".

Our native polecat resembles a large, heavily-built stoat, much darker in colour and with a shorter tail. Sometimes it is almost black, and though its under-parts are lighter they are never white. Like the stoat, the polecat gives off a disgusting scent which is so persistent that the fur of the polecat is of no value to the furrier. The animal is about twenty-two inches long and has an eight-inch tail.

Today, the polecat is one of our rarest animals, though it still inhabits the forests and thickets of Wales, Cumberland and the Scottish Highlands.

The Welsh polecats include a reddish-brown variety. In addition to poultry, rabbits and other game it catches and eats snakes and fish, including eels, but it kills more than it needs. It is, indeed, so fierce that it has been known to attack man.

Marten and Wildcat

The revolting smell of the polecat gave it its old name of "foumart" or "foul marten", for though the marten is not closely related to it the animals are roughly similar in size and shape. The marten also has a scent gland under its tail, but this gives a pleasant sweet smell rather like musk, so that the other name for this animal is "sweet marten". Because it lives chiefly in the forests, running about on the branches of trees, it is also known as the "pine marten".

However, in bleak mountainous districts it makes its nest among the boulders, employing its climbing powers to scale the rocks. It makes a rough nest in suitable places, but often takes over an old bird's nest or a squirrel's drey. It is a handsome creature with a long bushy tail like a fox's brush. Its colour is a rich brown with paler or buff under-parts. It is even rarer than the polecat, and is almost extinct.

Another rare British wild animal is the true wildcat, which must not be confused with the descendants of homeless domestic cats which have run wild. The wildcat is found only in the Highlands of Scotland, where it is now said to be increasing in numbers. Crosses between the wildcat and domestic cat are also found from time to time.

The wildcat resembles a domestic "tabby", except that it is larger and has stripes like a tiger's running across its stout forelegs and down its sides. It is extremely fierce and cannot be approached, coaxed or tamed. It inhabits the so-called "deer forests", which are moorlands almost devoid of trees, making a nest in a cave, a thicket of brushwood or a fox's old earth. Like other cats, it is not fond of water but, also like other cats, it can swim well when so minded.

Camouflage

No doubt the stripes of the wildcat, like the stripes of the tiger, help to conceal the animal by breaking up its outline and mimicking the stems of grasses and herbs, but in common with most other wild animals the wildcat is paler underneath and this also helps to make it invisible.

To see how this comes about, consider an object like a tennis-ball resting on a table. The top of the ball receives light from the window or sky, and is bright and clear, but the lower half of the ball is dark because it is in its own shadow. It is this contrast between light and shade which makes the ball look solid and "real".

Now, an animal is also rounded in form and casts a shadow, but if it has light under-parts these tend to counteract the darkness of the shadow. Thus, they reduce the effect of solidity, and the animal's pattern has a better chance of blending with its surroundings. If it is distinguished at all it must now be by its outline, and it will appear more or less flat as if cut out of cardboard.

These effects are seldom perfectly realized, but experiments made with models show that solid objects can be made to disappear entirely in this way when viewed from a short distance. There is no doubt that wild animals—and birds—are considerably helped by having white or pale under-parts, as well as by patterns on their fur.

Bats in the Belfry

Almost everybody who has been out in the late dusk has seen a bat in flight, though bats are sometimes mistaken for birds by the unobservant and by children. The flight of a bat is seldom in a straight line, but makes circles and swoops with a swift but somewhat "floppy" motion. The bat is not going anywhere—it is catching midges and other small insects which are still about in the late evening. Bats catch and eat all their food on the wing, and often fly all night feeding largely upon moths.

Usually several bats are seen together, for they are sociable animals and sleep by day in droves, often in the roof of an old barn, a church belfry or a dark cave. In such places they may sometimes be found hanging upside-down by their hind feet, their wings folded at their sides. The wings consist of a leathery skin stretched over greatly elongated fingers and connected to fore limbs, hind limbs and tail, so as to make a single large flying plane.

There are ten species of bats in Britain, two being very common all over the British Isles. These are the "pipistrelle" and the "long-eared" bat. The "noctule" or "great bat" is also common in England, and the "natterer's bat" and two species of "horseshoe bat" in Wales, the West Country and Ireland. The bat therefore holds a considerable place among the British wild animals. Though also called "flittermice", bats are not even remotely related to the mice, yet they look superficially very much like winged mice with very large ears.

FLYING "BLIND"

Their ears are very elaborate and extremely sensitive, for though bats are not blind their sight is very poor and they rely on their ears for guidance. They do this by uttering a very high squeak and then catching its echoes from surrounding objects. It is a sort of "radar", using sound waves instead of wireless waves, and it is so efficient that a bat can fly amongst a tangle of branches or wires in complete darkness without any risk of collision. The squeak of a bat comes almost in the ultrasonic range, being about 20,000 vibrations per second, and many people are quite unable to hear it.